The Spirit That Moves Us
READER

Seventh Anniversary Anthology

EDITED BY MORTY SKLAR

Offered to subscribers to *The Spirit That Moves Us* magazine, as Volume 6, Numbers 2 & 3

Other anthologies from The Spirit That Moves Us Press:

Editor's Choice: Literature & Graphics from the U. S. Small Press, 1965-1977 (published 1980)
Indexed in *Granger's Index to Poetry*, 7th edition.

The Actualist Anthology (poetry; published 1977)
Indexed in *Granger's Index to Poetry*, 7th edition.

Cross-Fertilization: The Human Spirit As Place
(poetry, fiction, essay, artwork; published 1980)

Forthcoming from The Spirit That Moves Us Press:

Nuke-Rebuke: Writers & Artists Against Nuclear Energy & Weapons (Spring 1983)

New Fiction (not yet titled; Fall 1983)

The Spirit That Moves Us Press, Inc.
P. O. Box 1585
Iowa City, Iowa 52244
(319) 338-5569

The Spirit That Moves Us
READER

Seventh Anniversary Anthology

EDITED BY MORTY SKLAR

104 Poems, Stories & Visuals from
The Spirit That Moves Us magazine
from 1975 to 1982

Including an Index to All Issues

The Spirit That Moves Us Press
Iowa City: 1982

Acknowledgements & Other Information

"The Cast Off," by Marge Piercy, reprinted in *The Moon Is Always Female*, is published here with permission from Alfred A. Knopf, Inc. (copyright 1980).

Gratitude is expressed to the following for assistance in the publication of this book:
The National Endowment for the Arts, a federal agency, for a matching grant.
The Iowa Arts Council, for a matching grant.
These local businesses and individuals, for donations of cash and services—Richard Winter, MD; Iowa State Bank; Jim Gilmore; Gilda Imports; Dain Bosworth, Inc.; Frohwein Office Supplies; Bill Gauger; Technigraphics.

The Spirit That Moves Us magazine (ISSN 0364-4014) is indexed in *Index of American Periodical Verse* and *Index to Periodical Fiction.* Volume 2, Nos. 2 & 3 (*The Actualist Anthology*) is indexed in *Granger's Index to Poetry*, 7th edition. All issues are available. Subscriptions may be placed thru The Spirit That Moves Us Press, or thru EBSCO, Faxon and other subscription agencies. Cost is $6 for individuals for 3 issues, and $8 for libraries.

All The Spirit That Moves Us books are available thru the press or thru Bookslinger in St. Paul. Selected titles may also be ordered thru other distributors, and found in bookstores and libraries throughout the U. S. and abroad.

Unsolicited manuscripts are always welcome. Include self-addressed, stamped envel.

Typesetting, design & layout by Morty Sklar.

Cover visual is by Stuart Mead.

First Edition, cloth and paper, November 1982

Number 4 of The Contemporary Anthology Series

Library of Congress Cataloging in Publication Data

Main entry under title:

A The Spirit that moves us reader.

(The Contemporary anthology series ; no. 4)
"96 poems, stories & visuals from the Spirit that moves us magazine, from 1975-1982."
Includes index.
1. Literature, Modern—20th century. 2. Spirit that moves us magazine—Indexes. 3. Spirit that moves us—Indexes. I. Sklar, Morty, 1935- . II. Spirit that moves us magazine. III. Spirit that moves us magazine. IV. Series.
PN6014.T355 1982 810'.8'0054 82-10685
ISBN 0-930370-13-9
ISBN 0-930370-14-7 (pbk.)
ISBN 0-930370-12-0 (signed, hand-bound, A-Z)

The Spirit That Moves Us Press, Inc., P. O. Box 1585, Iowa City, Iowa 52244

"The Little Magazine has been a central and primary feature of the modern movement in literature, and any serious record of that evolution . . . requires a full account of these magazines."

—*The New York Times*, October 15, 1976

"I try to find out something about man, including myself, and to pass it on. Writing means to write somebody. Writing means to cross borders, inside and outside. Writing means research-work for peace."

—*Wolfgang Kohlhaase*,
author living in East Germany, represented in this anthology

By Way of a Preface

"*The Spirit That Moves Us* is alive and well, an artistic success, if not a financial one . . . One folds back the first page of each issue confident that good poetry and fiction will follow . . . Sklar is a commanding editor whose care and patience in selecting the material for *TSTMU* is evident in each issue . . . Any library without *TSTMU* on its shelves is missing a significant voice on the national scene."

—**Serials Review**, Vol. 6, No. 4: 1980

"Sklar is a brilliant editor, and his periodical has taste and clarity . . . . Highly recommended for all libraries."

—**Magazines for Libraries**, 4th edition

"*Spirit* keeps getting kudos from everyone, and with good reason . . . . If you collect contemporary writing or little magazines, buy this magazine."

—Cristine Rom, **Serials Review**,
Summer 1982

"The poets are mostly younger and relatively unknown [although] well known people contribute, such as Marge Piercy, David Ray and Richard Kostelanetz . . . *The Spirit That Moves Us* is a good example of a little magazine whose editor lives for poetry, and it is well worth considering by libraries."

—**Choice** (A.L.A.), December 1980

". . . it has a warm, human tone throughout, yet nowhere is it sloppy or wasteful, and the amount of really significant work is much greater than in the average little magazine. Morty Sklar has an instinct, it seems, for what works—but without any hang-ups for or against certain 'schools.' If *The Spirit That Moves Us* keeps moving the way it has been, it should move itself right up among the most valuable and lasting magazines of poetry."

—**Small Press Review**, June/July 1976

Introduction

It has been a great pleasure for me to review issues of *The Spirit That Moves Us* published since its inception in 1975, for the purpose of compiling this anthology. From a magazine which at first drew mostly from the vital literary activity in Iowa City in the early to middle 1970s, inspired by the various and non-academic writing and the proliferation of other Little Magazines, *The Spirit That Moves Us* has expanded like a long poem, drawing from and reaching out to the literary community nation-wide and world-wide. Most of the work between its covers comes unsolicited, tho I am quick to solicit work from writers and visual artists whose work I admire.

I felt it important to have as a subtitle to this collection, *Seventh Anniversary Anthology*, because this book is not a salutation to a period which has ended, but a pause, and a celebration of what is and will continue to be as long as we can make it happen. The publication of any small-run, non-commercial literary magazine is obviously a labor of love, and its continuance not possible by 270 individual and library subscriptions and a hundred bookstore sales (ours, presently). Without assistance from the National Endowment for the Arts, the Iowa Arts Council, the Coordinating Council of Literary Magazines and local businesses and individuals, survival would in fact depend upon a publisher with money to invest, which neither I nor most others I know of, are.

The reader will note the absence of "best" in the title to this book. I love, and am proud of, every work published here, but several considerations went into the selection process. Among those considerations is space, and because of that, practically every contributor is represented by only one work. The living, for the most part, have been favored over the deceased. Works which are very similar in aim and style to other works in this book have not been included. And, given the fact that almost 500 works have been published in *The Spirit That Moves Us*, the reprinting of more than the 99 published here would seem to go beyond the intention of this collection.

Something should be said about how work is selected for inclusion in *The Spirit That Moves Us*. I believe there is no truly objective way to judge poetry, fiction and artwork. Basically, what I like to see is work which expresses concern for life and living, and which is skillfully put together. However, there is work which combines both these qualities which has not found its way into the pages of *The Spirit That Moves Us*, and that brings us to a third, indefinable quality. The best way I can describe it is in terms of a love relationship. There are people and things which might have all the qualities for which we feel we could love them, such as concerns and attitudes which we hold dear, yet we don't love them. We might respect them and value their qualities, but we don't experience a very special feeling for them. Why? That is a good question, and that too is the crux of the editorial question. It is much more difficult to reject work of this kind than to reject work which is more obviously not to our liking.

For the reader who is not acquainted with limited edition, noncommercial literary magazines or presses, I would like to encourage the perusal of *The International Directory of Little Magazines and Small Presses* and *The Small Press Record of Books in Print*, as well as the catalog from the Coordinating Council of Literary Magazines, and his/her local public and university library and bookstore. The reader is also referred to *Editor's Choice: Literature & Graphics from the U. S. Small Press, 1965-1977* (published 1980; The Spirit That Moves Us Press) and *The Pushcart Prize* (published annually; The Pushcart Press). News and reviews of small presses may be seen in *American Book Review; New Pages: News and Reviews of the Progressive Book Trade; San Francisco Review of Books; Small Press Review; Contact II; Gargoyle; Coda; COSMEP Newsletter; Sipapu; Stony Hills; Small Press News; Home Grown Books; The Midwest Bookwatch; The Bloomsbury Review;* the column, "Magazines," by Bill Katz, in *Library Journal*; "Small Press Roundup," by Susan Shafarzek, in the December 15 issue of *Library Journal*; the "At a Glance" column by Cristine Rom, in *Serials Review*, as well as regular reviews of Little Magazines in *Serials Review*; and others. Many of the publications I have mentioned are listed in *The International Directory of Little Magazines and Small Presses*. Occasional Small Press focuses appear in *Publishers Weekly, The Christian Science Monitor* and other publications. *The Washington Post, The Los Angeles Times, West Coast Review of Books* and other major newspapers and magazines regularly carry reviews of Small Press publications.

Morty Sklar
Iowa City, 1982

For my wife,
Shelley Sterling-Sklar

We had all the possibilities in the world
except one
which we took

—Agneta Ara / Volume 4, Numbers 2 & 3
tr. from the Swedish by Lennart Bruce

Merrill Spector / original size / Volume 5, Number 3

CONTENTS

James Harrison / 56% of original / Volume 3, Number 3

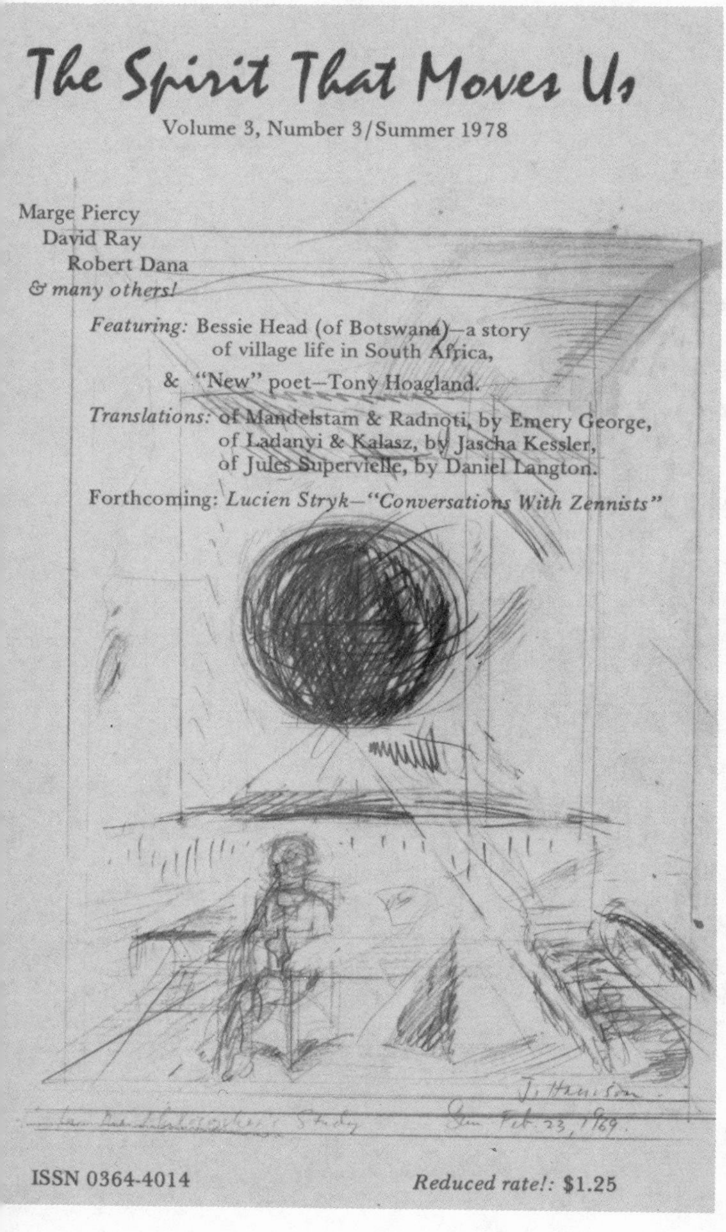
The Spirit That Moves Us

Volume 3, Number 3/Summer 1978

Marge Piercy
David Ray
Robert Dana
& many others!

Featuring: Bessie Head (of Botswana)—a story of village life in South Africa,

& "New" poet—Tony Hoagland.

Translations: of Mandelstam & Radnoti, by Emery George,
of Ladanyi & Kalasz, by Jascha Kessler,
of Jules Supervielle, by Daniel Langton.

Forthcoming: *Lucien Stryk—"Conversations With Zennists"*

ISSN 0364-4014

Reduced rate!: **$1.25**

David Kresh

VIEW OF SPRING GARDEN STREET

Volume 3, Number 3

The green sky foams with light
above Spring Garden Street
in the City of Brotherly Love imagined
in the wild eye of an exile. Painted
columns peel in the green light.
The blind man moves in stately rage
among the children smashing empty
bottles and screaming MOTHER MOTHER
YOUR MOTHER
                    Yesterday everyone danced
to nothing you can say can tear me away
from my guy. Tomorrow everyone will dance
to baby baby baby where did our
love go? Today the little girls
are jumping whipcracking rope:
LATE last NITE andthe NITE beFORE
MET my BAbyatthe CANdy STORE
how many sodas did we drink
ONE CRACK TWO CRACK THREE CRACK FOUR
CRACK pennies explode against a wall.
Leaning on a red car, bending
to the mirror, a thin brown child
in an orange shirt tucks a rose
behind his ear. Above his head,
above the night-blooming neon of Spring
Garden Street, the green sky
foams, swells, and blossoms into thunder.

Marge Piercy

THE CAST OFF

Volume 3, Number 3

This is a day to celebrate can-
openers, those lantern-jawed long-tailed
humping tools that cut through what keeps
us from what we need: a can of beans
trapped in its armor taunts the nails
and teeth of a hungry woman.

Today let us hear hurrahs for zippers,
those small shark teeth that part
politely to let us at what we want;
the tape on packages that unlock
us birthday presents; envelopes
we slit to thaw the frozen
words on the tundra of paper.

Today let us praise the small
rebirths, the emerging groundhog
from the sodden burrow; the nut
picked from the broken fortress of walnut
shell, itself pried from the oily fruit
shaken from the high turreted
city of the tree.

Today let us honor the safe whose door
hangs ajar; the champagne bottle
with its cork bounced off the ceiling
and into the soup tureen; the Victorian lady
in love who has removed her hood, her cloak,
her laced boots, her stockings, her overdress,
her underdress, her wool petticoat, her linen
petticoats, her silk petticoats, her whale bone
corset, her bustle, her chemise, her drawers, and
who still wants to! Today let us praise the cast

that finally opens, slit neatly in two
like a dinosaur egg, and out at last
comes somewhat hairier, powdered in dead skin
but still beautiful, the lost for months
body of my love.

Mihalyi Ladanyi

NO DENYING

Volume 3, Number 3

I lived at a time when
    poets had descended Parnassus
    and businessmen
    were junketing up to Parnassus.
In the era of the hiss I went round yelling *ed vivat!*
    and so led my rude life–
    beauty's drifting man.
I hated that bum's get-up, but anyhow
    the wind could drench me, and
    I could feel free again, a sailor.

When moonlight wavered over the tiled roofs
    and paused on the bleared walls
and I floated along between windows,
    my heart turned like a crazy compass.
Sighs echoing from those windows
    seemed the Sirens singing enchantingly–
what can I say? I think there's no denying
    I too might have been nominated
    President of the Poets' Chapter
                of the Writers' Union . . . .
but at that time I could live on bread and bacongrease,
    besides, my poor love
    would have seemed awkward
    in the glare of the spotlight with me.
So, we never aimed to augment our glory,
    and we felt quite okay in this dazzling
    nothingness.

Loitering along those obscure streets
    we were greeted,
    and they nodded back
    if we nodded first at them.

I sang them my song:
    and people sometimes said:
    "Oh, let Ladanyi scribble his anarchist doggerel . . . ."
On we wandered, anxious too,
    scared that one fine day
    even that society might drop off astern . . . .
We kept warm, curled up nights in close alleys
    like varmints scared by winter's onset
while hockshops bid
    for our ratty things
and our bundle of books dribbled back to the used shelf,
though by the time the cash came through
    night had long been there
    and all the stores were shut.
At those hours I wrote my poems,
    defiant, on fire,
    dreaming through the famished darkness
in the City of Clever Concerns–
    beauty's drifter.

–translated from the Magyar by Jascha Kessler

Robert Dana

HORSES

Volume 3, Number 3

Horses of earth
Horses of water
Great horses of grey cloud

A blizzard of horses

Dust
and the ponies of dust
Horses of muscle and blood

Chestnuts Roans Blacks
Palominos
Wild dapple of Appaloosas

Spanish ponies
cow-ponies
Broncs Mustangs
Arabians Morgans Tennessee Walkers
Trotters
Shetlands
Massive matched Percherons

Horses
and the names of horses
Whirlaway Man O'War Coaltown
Cannonero
Foolish Pleasure

Horses with tails of smoke
The giddy laughter of horses

Horses of war
their necks clothed in thunder

nostrils wide

The ground beneath them
terrible to look on

Horses of anger
Horses of cruelty
wringing the iron bit in their mouths

The horses of Psyche

Blake's horses
The horses of instruction
Horses of breath

Dawn horses

And the one horse in the heart

that runs
and runs

Barbara Unger

RIDING THE PENN CENTRAL RAILROAD INTO NEW YORK CITY

Volume 3, Number 3

West on the Hudson's
nuclear radiance
pleasure craft dot the river.

The Palisades
enclose the Western shore.

White wake of a motor boat
reminds her of the picnics
of last summer.
She can still taste
the salt spray
on her lips.

Now she rides alone
to the broken city.
Bankrupt train creeps
along the water's edge
into the slums of The Bronx.

Last week kid terrorists shot
the man in the first car.
Today they only hurl bottles,
shattering a window or two.
There is talk of bullet-proof glass.

Forward is freedom
through the dark tunnel.
What can you sacrifice,
woman,
freedom
rider?

Bessie Head

LIFE

Volume 3, Number 3

IN 1963, when the borders were first set up between Botswana and South Africa, pending Botswana's independence in 1966, all Botswana-born citizens had to return home. Everything had been mingled up in the old colonial days, and the traffic of people to and fro between the two countries had been a steady flow for years and years. More often, especially if they were migrant labourers working in the mines, their period of settlement was brief, but many people had settled there in permanent employment. It was these settlers who were disrupted and sent back to village life in a mainly rural country. On their return they brought with them bits and bits of a foreign culture and city habits which they had absorbed. Village people reacted in their own way; what they liked, and was beneficial to them—they absorbed, for instance, the faith-healing cult churches which instantly took hold like wildfire—what was harmful to them, they rejected. The murder of Life had this complicated undertone of rejection.

Life had left the village as a little girl of ten years old with her parents for Johannesburg. They had died in the meanwhile, and on Life's return, seventeen years later, she found, as was village custom, that she still had a home in the village. On mentioning that her name was Life Morapedi, the villagers immediately and obligingly took her to the Morapedi yard in the central part of the village. The family yard had remained intact, just as they had left it, except that it looked pathetic in its desolation. The thatch of the mud huts had patches of soil over them where the ants had made their nests; the wooden poles that supported the rafters of the huts had tilted to an angle as their base had been eaten through by the ants. The rubber hedge had grown to a disproportionate size and enclosed the yard in a gloom of shadows that kept out the sunlight. Weeds and grass of many seasonal rains entangled themselves in the yard.

Life's future neighbours, a group of women, continued to stand near her.

"We can help you to put your yard in order," they said kindly. "We are very happy that a child of ours has returned home."

They were impressed with the smartness of this city girl. They generally wore old clothes and kept their very best things for special occasions like weddings, and even then those best things might just be ordinary cotton prints. The girl wore an expensive cream costume of linen material, tailored to fit her tall, full figure. She had a bright, vivacious friendly manner and laughed freely and loudly. Her speech was rapid and a little hysterical but that was in keeping with her whole personality.

"She is going to bring us a little light," the women said among themselves, as they went off to fetch their work tools. They were always looking "for the light" and by that they meant that they were ever alert to receive new ideas that would freshen up the ordinariness and everydayness of village life.

A woman who lived near the Morapedi yard had offered Life hospitality until her own yard was set in order. She picked up the shining new suitcases and preceded Life to her own home, where Life was immediately surrounded with all kinds of endearing attentions—a low stool was placed in a shady place for her to sit on; a little girl came shyly forward with a bowl of water for her to wash her hands; and following on this, a tray with a bowl of meat and porridge was set before her so that she could revive herself after her long journey home. The other women briskly entered her yard with hoes to scratch out the weeds and grass, baskets of earth and buckets of water to resmear the mud walls, and they had found two idle men to rectify the precarious tilt of the wooden poles of the mud hut. These were the sort of gestures people always offered, but they were pleased to note that the newcomer seemed to have an endless stream of money which she flung around generously. The work party in her yard would suggest that the meat of a goat, slowly simmering in a great iron pot, would help the work to move with a swing, and Life would immediately produce the money to purchase the goat and also tea, milk, sugar, pots of porridge or anything the workers expressed a preference for, so that those two weeks of making Life's yard beautiful for her seemed like one long wedding-feast; people usually only ate that much at weddings.

"How is it you have so much money, our child?" one of the women at last asked, curiously.

"Money flows like water in Johannesburg," Life replied, with her gay and hysterical laugh. "You just have to know how to get it."

The women received this with caution. They said among themselves that their child could not have lived a very good life in Johannesburg. Thrift and honesty were the dominant themes of village life and everyone knew that one could not be honest and rich at the same time; they counted every penny and knew how they had acquired it—with hard work. They never imagined money as a bottomless pit without end; it always had an end and was hard to come by in this dry, semi-desert land. They predicted that she would soon settle down—intelligent girls got jobs in the post office sooner or later.

Life had had the sort of varied career that a city like Johannesburg offered a lot of black women. She had been a singer, beauty queen, advertising model, and prostitute. None of these careers were available in the village—for the illiterate women there was farming and housework; for the literate, teaching, nursing, and clerical work. The first wave of women Life attracted to herself were the farmers and housewives. They were the intensely conservative hard-core centre of village life. It did not take them long to shun her completely because men started turning up in an unending stream. What caused a stir of amazement was that Life was the first and the only woman in the village to make a business out of selling herself. The men were paying her for her services. People's attitude toward sex was broad and generous—it was recognised as a necessary part of human life, that it ought to be available whenever possible like food and water, or else one's life would be extinguished or one would get dreadfully ill. To prevent these catastrophes from happening, men and women generally had quite a lot of sex but on a respectable and human level, with financial considerations coming in as an afterthought. When the news spread around that this had now become a business in Life's yard, she attracted to herself a second wave of women—the beer-brewers of the village.

The beer-brewing women were a gay and lovable crowd who had emancipated themselves some time ago. They were drunk every day and could be seen staggering around the village, usually with a wide-eyed, illegitimate baby hitched on to their hips. They also talked and laughed loudly and slapped each other on the back and had developed a language all their own:

"Boyfriends, yes. Husbands, uh, uh, no. Do this! Do that! We want to rule ourselves."

But they too were subject to the respectable order of village life. Many men passed through their lives but they were all for a time steady boyfriends. The usual arrangement was:

"Mother, you help me and I'll help you."

This was just so much eye-wash. The men hung around, lived on the resources of the women, and during all this time they would part with about R2.00 of their own money. After about three months a tally-up would be made:

"Boyfriend," the woman would say, "Love is love and money is money. You owe me money." And he'd never be seen again, but another scoundrel would take his place. And so the story went on and on. They found their queen in Life and like all queens, they set her activities apart from themselves; they never attempted to extract money from the constant stream of men because they did not know how, but they liked her yard. Very soon the din and riot of a Johannesburg township was duplicated, on a minor scale, in the central part of the village. A transistor radio blared the day long. Men and women reeled around drunk and laughing and food and drink flowed like milk and honey. The people of the surrounding village watched this phenomenon with pursed lips and commented darkly:

"They'll all be destroyed one day like Sodom and Gomorrah."

Life, like the beer-brewing women, had a language of her

own too. When her friends expressed surprise at the huge quantities of steak, eggs, liver, kidneys, and rice they ate in her yard —the sort of food they too could now and then afford but would not dream of purchasing—she replied in a carefree, offhand way: "I'm used to handling big money." They did not believe it; they were too solid to trust this kind of luck which had such shaky foundations, and as though to offset some doom that might be just around the corner they often brought along their own scraggy, village chickens reared in their yards, as offerings for the day's round of meals. And one of Life's philosophies on life, which they were to recall with trembling a few months later, was: "My motto is: live fast, die young, and have a goodlooking corpse." All this was said with the bold, free joy of a woman who had broken all the social taboos. They never followed her to those dizzy heights.

A few months after Life's arrival in the village, the first hotel with its pub opened. It was initially shunned by all the women and even the beer-brewers considered they hadn't fallen *that* low yet—the pub was also associated with the idea of selling oneself. It became Life's favourite business venue. It simplified the business of making appointments for the following day. None of the men questioned their behaviour, nor how such an unnatural situation had been allowed to develop—they could get all the sex they needed for free in the village, but it seemed to fascinate them that they should pay for it for the first time. They had quickly got to the stage where they communicated with Life in short-hand language:

"When?" And she would reply: "Ten o'clock." "When?" "Two o'clock." "When?" "Four o'clock," and so on.

And there would be the roar of cheap small talk and much buttock slapping. It was her element and her feverish, glittering, brilliant black eyes swept around the bar, looking for everything and nothing at the same time.

Then one evening death walked quietly into the bar. It was Lesego, the cattle-man, just come in from his cattle-post, where he had been occupied for a period of three months. Men built up their own, individual reputations in the village and Lesego's was one of the most respected and honoured. People said of him: "When Lesego has got money and you need it, he will give you what he has got and he won't trouble you about the date of payment . . . " He was honoured for another reason also —for the clarity and quiet indifference of his thinking. People often found difficulty in sorting out issues or the truth in any debatable matter. He had a way of keeping his head above water, listening to an argument and always pronouncing the final judgment: "Well, the truth about this matter is . . . " He was also one of the most successful cattle-men with a balance of R7.000 in the bank, and whenever he came into the village he lounged around and gossiped or attended village kgotla meetings, so that people had a saying: "Well, I must be getting about my business. I'm not like Lesego with money in the bank."

As usual, the brilliant radar eyes swept feverishly around the bar. They did the rounds twice that evening in the same manner, each time coming to a dead stop for a full second on the thin, dark concentrated expression of Lesego's face. There wasn't any other man in the bar with that expression; they all had sheepish, inane-looking faces. He was the nearest thing she had seen for a long time to the Johannesburg gangsters she had associated with—the same small, economical gestures, the same power and control. All the men near him quieted down and began to consult with him in low earnest voices; they were talking about the news of the day which never reached the remote cattle-posts. Whereas all the other men had to approach her, the third time her radar eyes swept round he stood his ground, turned his head slowly, and then jerked it back slightly in a silent command:

"Come here."

She moved immediately to his end of the bar.

"Hullo," he said, in an astonishingly tender voice and a smile flickered across his dark, reserved face. That was the sum total of Lesego, that basically he was a kind and tender man, that he liked women and had been so successful in that sphere that he took his dominance and success for granted. But they looked at each other from their own worlds and came to fatal conclusions—she saw in him the power and maleness of the gangsters; he saw the freshness and surprise of an entirely new kind of woman. He had left all his women after a time because they bored him, and like all people who live an ordinary humdrum life, he was attracted to that undertone of hysteria in her.

Very soon they stood up and walked out together. A shocked silence fell upon the bar. The men exchanged looks with each other and the way these things communicate themselves, they knew that all the other appointments had been cancelled while Lesego was there. And as though speaking their thoughts aloud, Sianana, one of Lesego's friends commented: "Lesego just wants to try it out like we all did because it is something new. He won't stay there when he finds out that it is rotten to the core."

But Sianana was to find out that he did not fully understand his friend. Lesego was not seen at his usual lounging-places for a week and when he emerged again it was to announce that he was to marry. The news was received with cold hostility. Everyone talked of nothing else; it was as impossible as if a crime was being committed before their very eyes. Sianana once more made himself the spokesman. He waylaid Lesego on his way to the village kgotla:

"I am much surprised by the rumours about you, Lesego," he said bluntly. "You can't marry that woman. She's a terrible fuck-about!"

Lesego stared back at him steadily, then he said in his quiet, indifferent way: "Who isn't here?"

Sianana shrugged his shoulders. The subleties were beyond him; but whatever else was going on it wasn't commercial, it was human, but did that make it any better? Lesego liked to bugger up an argument like that with a straightforward point. As they walked along together Sianana shook his head several times to indicate that something important was eluding him, until at last with a smile, Lesego said: "She has told me all about her bad ways. They are over."

Sianana merely compressed his lips and remained silent.

Life made the announcement too, after she was married, to all her beer-brewing friends: "All my old ways are over," she said. "I have now become a woman."

She still looked happy and hysterical. Everything came to her too easily, men, money, and now marriage. The beer-brewers were not slow to point out to her with the same amazement with which they had exclaimed over the steak and eggs, that there were many women in the village who had cried their eyes out over Lesego. She was very flattered.

Their lives, at least Lesego's, did not change much with marriage. He still liked lounging around the village; the rainy season had come and life was easy for the cattle-men at this time because there was enough water and grazing for the animals. He wasn't the kind of man to fuss about the house and during this time he only made three pronouncements about the household. He took control of all the money. She had to ask him for it and state what it was to be used for. Then he didn't like the transistor radio blaring the whole day long.

"Women who keep that thing going the whole day have nothing in their heads," he said.

Then he looked down at her from a great height and commented finally and quietly: "If you go with those men again, I'll kill you."

This was said so indifferently and quietly, as though he never really expected his authority and dominance to encounter any challenge.

She hadn't the mental equipment to analyse what had hit her, but something seemed to strike her a terrible blow behind the head. She instantly succumbed to the blow and rapidly began to fall apart. On the surface, the everyday round of village life was deadly dull in its even, unbroken monotony; one day slipped easily into another, drawing water, stamping corn, cooking food. But within this there were enormous tugs and pulls between people. Custom demanded that people care about each other, and all day long there was this constant traffic of people in and out of each other's lives. Someone had to be buried; sympathy and help were demanded for this event—there were money loans, new-born babies, sorrow, trouble, gifts. Lesego had long been the king of this world; there was, every day, a long string of people, wanting something or wanting to give him something in gratitude for a past favour. It was the basic strength of village life. It created people whose sympathetic and emotional responses were always fully awakened, and it rewarded them by richly filling in a void that was one big, gaping yawn. When the hysteria and cheap rowdiness were taken away, Life fell into the yawn; she had nothing inside herself to cope with this way of life that had finally caught up with her. The beer-brewing women were still there; they still liked her yard because Lesego was casual and easy-going and all that went on in it now—like the old men squatting in corners with gifts: "Lesego, I had good luck with my hunting today. I caught two rabbits and I want to share one with you . . . "—was simply the Tswana way of life they too lived. In keeping with their queen's new status, they said: "We are women and must do something."

They collected earth and dung and smeared and decorated Life's courtyard. They drew water for her, stamped her corn, and things looked quite ordinary on the surface because Lesego also liked a pot of beer. No one noticed the expression of anguish that had crept into Life's face. The boredom of the daily round was almost throttling her to death and no matter which way she looked, from the beer-brewers to her husband to all the people who called, she found no one with whom she could communicate what had become an actual physical pain. After a month of it, she was near collapse. One morning she mentioned her agony to the beer-brewers: "I think I have made a mistake. Married life doesn't suit me."

And they replied sympathetically: "You are just getting used to it. After all it's a different life in Johannesburg."

The neighbours went further. They were impressed by a marriage they thought could never succeed. They started saying that one never ought to judge a human being who was both good and bad, and Lesego had turned a bad woman into a good woman which was something they had never seen before. Just as they were saying this and nodding their approval, Sodom and Gomorrah started up all over again. Lesego had received word late in the evening that the new born calves at his cattle-post were dying, and early the next morning he was off again in his truck.

The old, reckless wild woman awakened from a state near death with a huge sigh of relief. The transistor blared, the food flowed again, the men and women reeled around dead drunk. Simply by their din they beat off all the unwanted guests who nodded their heads grimly. When Lesego came back they were going to tell him this was no wife for him.

Three days later Lesego unexpectedly was back in the village. The calves were all anaemic and they had to be brought in to the vet for an injection. He drove his truck straight through the village to the vet's camp. One of the beer-brewers saw him and hurried in alarm to her friend.

"The husband is back," she whispered fearfully, pulling Life to one side.

"Agh," she replied irritably.

She did dispel the noise, the men, and the drink, but a wild anger was driving her to break out of a way of life that was like death to her. She told one of the men she'd see him at six o'clock. At about five o'clock Lesego drove into the yard with the calves. There was no one immediately around to greet him. He jumped out of the truck and walked to one of the huts, pushing open the door. Life was sitting on the bed. She looked up silently and sullenly. He was a little surprised but his mind was still distracted by the calves. He had to settle them in the yard for the night.

"Will you make some tea," he said. "I'm very thirsty."

"There's no sugar in the house," she said. "I'll have to get some."

Something irritated him but he hurried back to the calves and his wife walked out of the yard. Lesego had just settled the calves when a neighbour walked in, he was very angry.

"Lesego," he said bluntly, "we told you not to marry that woman. If you go to the yard of Radithobolo now you'll find her in bed with him. Go and see for yourself that you may leave that bad woman!"

Lesego stared quietly at him for a moment, then at his own pace as though there were no haste or chaos in his life, he went to the hut they used as a kitchen. A tin full of sugar stood there. He turned and found a knife in the corner, one of the large ones he used for slaughtering cattle, and slipped it into his shirt. Then at his own pace he walked to the yard of Radithobolo. It looked deserted, except that the door of one of the huts was partially open and one closed. He kicked open the door of the closed hut and the man within shouted out in alarm. On seeing Lesego he sprang cowering into a corner. Lesego jerked his head back indicating that the man should leave the room. But Radithobolo did not run far. He wanted to enjoy himself so he pressed himself into the shadows of the rubber hedge. He expected the usual husband-and-wife scene—the irate husband cursing at the top of his voice; the wife, hysterical in her lies and self-defence. Only then Lesego walked out of the yard and he held in his hand a huge, blood-stained knife. On seeing the knife Radithobolo immediately fell to the ground in a dead faint. There were a few people on the footpath and they shrank into the rubber hedge at the sight of that knife.

Very soon a wail arose. People clutched at their heads and began running in all directions crying yo! yo! yo! in their shock. It was some time before anyone thought of calling the police. They were so disordered because murder, outright and violent, was a most uncommon and rare occurence in village life. It seemed that only Lesego kept cool that evening. He was sitting quietly in his yard when the whole police force came tearing in. They looked at him in horror and began to thoroughly upbraid him for looking so unperturbed.

"You have taken a human life and you are cool like that!" they said angrily. "You are going to hang by the neck for this. It's a serious crime to take a human life."

He did not hang by the neck. He kept that cool, head-above-water indifferent look, right up to the day of his trial. Then he looked up at the judge and said calmly: "Well, the truth of the matter is, I had just returned from the cattle-post. I had had trouble with my calves that day. I came home late and being thirsty, asked my wife to make me tea. She said there was no sugar in the house and left to buy some. My neighbour, Mathata came in after this and said that my wife was not at the shops but in the yard of Radithobolo. I thought I would check up about the sugar first and in the kitchen I found a tin full of it. I was sorry and surprised to see this. Then a fire seemed to fill my heart. I thought that if she was doing a bad thing with Radithobolo as Mathata said, I'd better kill her because I cannot understand a wife who could be so corrupt . . ."

Lesego had been doing this for years, passing judgment on all aspects of life in his straightforward, uncomplicated way. The judge, who was a white man, and therefore not involved in Tswana custom and its debates, was as much impressed by Lesego's manner as all the village men had been.

"This is a crime of passion," he said sympathetically. "So there are extenuating circumstances. But it is still a serious crime to take a human life so I sentence you to five years imprisonment . . ."

Lesego's friend, Sianana, who was to take care of his business affairs while he was in jail, came to visit Lesego still shaking his head. Something was eluding him about the whole business, as though it had been planned from the very beginning.

"Lesego," he said, with deep sorrow, "why did you kill that fuck-about? You had legs to walk away. You could have walked away. Are you trying to show us that rivers never cross here? There are good women and good men but they seldom join their lives together. It's always this mess and foolishness . . ."

A song by Jim Reeves was very popular at that time: *That's What Happens When Two Worlds Collide*. When they were drunk, the beer-brewing women used to sing it and start weeping. Maybe they had the last word on the whole affair.

Tony Hoagland

WHEN TRAVELLING

Volume 3, Number 3

I carry the buddha and a flask
of Jack Daniels, a stack of books
in a black leather bag.

I carry more than I can
for a little ways,
then less,
in case I want to stay.

I know I am travelling
through the giant house of my life
where I climb on a plane
to get to a certain room.

On board, I am given a plate
covered with food;
I flip through a few pages of roast beef
to find the turquoise green beans;
they are beautiful and inert;
You would like a necklace of them, I think;
I eat two helpings.

Below, the cities glitter
like smashed things;
erased by the wing moving
forward like a black shore.

I ask no questions
and the stewardesses smile
through the holes in their beautiful masks.
They are like beautiful horses
all raised on the same tropical island,
bred for color and balance;

I can see them running on the beach,
their lean bodies the color of lobster thermadore,
surf foaming in the background . . .

A drink appears in front of me;
ice chunks in the hand of an angel
brown juice splashing over the rocks

& then the performance begins:
the dance of the oxygen masks.
Orange cups appear on clear plastic tubes
One whispers the other depicts
Cover your nose and mouth, they imply,
swaying forward down the aisle;

The virgin in the blue paper uniform
points symbolically over our heads
the hidden life vests; the floatable cushions;
Her fingers are like brown magic markers;
her hips suggest the location of emergency exits;
something of the cold air beyond them . . .

We hold onto our seatbelts;
we know we are under protection
The captain interrupts us.
He is from the south
which is to our west, he says,
laughing like a car.
We are coming down.
The ground full of puddles
approaches.
I keep being interrupted in my story.
Where this one lands,
another one begins.

Ann Struthers

THE DANCE

Volume 3, Number 3

All of us farm girls
put on our glad rags
and go into town.
It's Saturday night,
and there's a dance in Stratman's Hall.

Wild Bill got fired yesterday,
that wild kid from nowhere.
Wild Bill broke his pitchfork handle
across the nose
of Dad's fancy strawberry roan.

We dance with the boys
who wear clean jeans and clean
shirts, and the band plays
LOUD.
The men smell of beer
and sweat in the August night.
Dearie McClay is dancing drunk,
the Peterson twins start a fight,
Eddie Bolinsky, shirt sleeves
rolled to his armpits, flexes his muscles.
But Wild Bill isn't there, that wild kid.

Osip Mandelstam

ADMIRALTY BUILDING

Volume 3, Number 3

In the northern capital a dusty silver poplar
Pines away; caught in its leaves, a clock's transparent dial.
And amidst the dark green, frigate or acropolis,
It shines from far off, kin to water and sky.

Castle of air and touch-me-not tower,
Serving a line of successors to Peter,
It shows us that beauty is not a demigod's whimsy
But the fierce eye-measure of a simple carpenter.

Over four elements we maintain friendly sway,
But it was a free man who added a fifth.
Isn't there an outline, an excellence of space,
Drawn about this shrine, built in perfect wisdom?

Angrily the fretful Medousai hang on;
Like abandoned plows, the mooring anchors rust.
And behold, the bonds of three fathoms dissolve,
And all the world's oceans open up.

—translated from the Russian by Emery George

The Spirit That Moves Us
Volume 3, Numbers 1 & 2: Fall/Winter, '77/'78
Walt Whitman: by Chilean, Carlos Hermosilla Alvarez
ISSN 0364-4014
64 pages
$1.75

Floyd Skloot

EXECUTIVE SEARCH

Volume 3, Numbers 1 & 2

You are an executive
This is not your city
It belongs to other executives
But you talk the same language

(time/motion studies
organizational models
zero base budgeting
MBO PPB A-95s)

The hotel is familiar
Convention facilities adequate
Ball game across the freeway
New films downtown
Last year's in your room

You are here as one result
of a $50,000 Executive Search
A field of five finalists
Brought before the Board
For Public scrutiny

On paper you looked acceptable
In person you have slimmed down
Enough to justify the new suit
They say the first screen
Is easy by comparison
Now the Board gets its crack at you

You have handled these questions before
So you are confident of no surprises
You have noted the Board is balanced
There are women, Blacks, old, young

Even one Latino and a priest

You can sit and know
There is nothing to worry about

Ahmos Zu-Bolton

THE BASKETBALL STAR

Volume 3, Numbers 1 & 2

We define:
Livewire Davis. The one
with the million-dollar jump-shot.

Livewire as bebop star:
torn between his body's genius
for fast breaks
and a questionmark
called rage. Stumbling
thru a lifetime of all-star games
(he never hit the winning points
but was always a frontpager.

Livewire's days
were lawless theatre
(except for the 8 o'clock class,
except for the poetry of bullshitting
with the women,
except for the ritual of practice:
run jump "shoot their eyes out"
defense
defense
except for the terrible puzzle of books
he was free.

Susan North

CHAINS

Volume 3, Numbers 1 & 2

The court date was set in October
and you have had time to prepare.
You wear the blue suit and no jewelry.
If he is freed, he will be home for Christmas.

You enter the courtroom, choosing a seat by yourself.
There is a clock with large roman numerals,
a sign which forbids smoking. You hear the chains
before the guard opens the door.

You have rehearsed this moment a thousand times.
You will not look at his hands.
You meet his eyes and smile.
He looks frozen or dead.

You try to concentrate on the testimony
but the voices fade. You think of your stuffed bear
torn apart by the neighbor's hound,
and how heavy the gun is,
the perspiration stains on your graduation dress,
stones rattling in a tin can,
how to make room in the closet for his clothes again,
how it will be to touch him.

The proceedings are over. The lawyer
shakes hands with the prosecutor.
Your husband is smiling. You try
to respond but sawdust spurts from your arm.
The room darkens and the sound of chains rises
like an orchestra.

He keeps smiling
but the chains are up to his neck.

Has he forgotten the signal?
You will have to act on your own.
Christmas is coming.

Joseph Bruchac

TONAWANDA

Volume 3, Numbers 1 & 2

The strings of wampum
which belonged to Handsome Lake
tell the Good Message.
No white has ever seen them.

At Tonawanda
they may be brought out
once each two years
at the beginning
of the circuit of preaching
the prophet's words
from Longhouse to Longhouse
which begins each fall.
He who bears the title Ganio'dai'io
is their custodian.

Yet if even one cloud
is in the sky
the strings may not
be brought into the open.

Whenever an anthropologist
is present at that meeting
there is always one small cloud
which can be found.

James Bertolino

THE POEM ABOUT DUST

Volume 3, Numbers 1 & 2

She glides through chambers
of astonishment,
the simple rooms
where sunlight defines
its love for dust.

All syllables spoken here
still orbit
their closest things.

She feels a varied humming
as her limbs pull
through the fields of floor lamp, wine
bottle, cutting board
& chair.

She will never be alone here,
where the air
has voices, & surfaces
are wonderful
with velvety landscapes of dust.

Her slightest touch, each breath
draws cheers from
this universe
where her movement is the only rule.

Dennis Cooper

BILLY McCALL'S SUMMER

Volume 3, Numbers 1 & 2

at twenty-two
this is your summer.
the merry-go-round of girls
slows around you.
you see their faces.
teeshirts are you.
sideburns go in june;
long hair a month later.
now god falls for you,
promoting you to sex symbol.
girls from your childhood
reappear as good women.
laura sucks your ass.
mishima changes your life.
you are no longer eighteen
and the confusion clears.
drugs were a pretty good game.
school was worth it.
terry was in love with you.
you are willing to sleep now,
unafraid of missing something.
you are going to be rude forever.
rock music rules you.
the stones are back after three years
and better than ever.
you stand on your seat and dance.
as august ends one girl
is sleeping with you.
your job as stock boy continues.
there are no signs of death
in you, only energy
and pleasure controlled.
it's great to see you like this

and be among your friends this summer,
to settle with the dust around you

Floyd C. Stuart

THE WIVES

Volume 3, Numbers 1 & 2

They pass and the air smells
sweet for a moment. Their kids thrash
in the pool: it throbs
like an ocean liner's propellor.
The women lie on their stomachs
and reach back to undo straps.
They plunge into the heavy shudder of sun.
Some relent to the arms of tubular chairs.
Their eyes are closed.
Their lips stare
in near smile
at the heat's weight.
They look wise,
as if about to speak
of weakness and power.

Husbands are working,
there are few men.
The women are drawn
in a wagon train circle.
They are wives, and keep
a certain reserve.
The lifeguards see it.
It is like a knitting needle
stabbed in yarn.

But the women languidly oil their legs,
their fingers rejoicing over spills of bosom.
They turn on their sides and pour
oil on the flare of their hips.
They know they are the lifeguards'
rack and screw.
A toddler chokes on water.

His mother presses
the male-child's head
into the jelly of her breasts,
proud to comfort and subdue.

They rarely swim.
After they do, the water rounds
on them like a sweat of honey.

They like being women without their men.
As they talk of divorce
or books or supper,
they seem to love each other.
A silence comes.
The sun beats as they rise
in their bodies like yeast.
They reach . . . they reach . . .

But they can see dust eddy into their navels.
Already their toes have the curl
and knob of dry weeds.
The faces of men are bird-pecked berries.
At five they leave.
The lengthening shadows of trees
are bars clanged across
their path to the parking lot.

Some of them think of their husbands
(who love them) in bed,
the male back a taut bow
in their hands. They know
how the men feel
(shoulders so hard, so
sad) in the moan
of letting go.

Michael Grimes

AN ENDORSEMENT FOR PUDDING

Volume 3, Numbers 1 & 2

Lying on the sofa now,
Bathing in the gray light of the television,
Watching Humphrey Bogart say goodbye to Ingrid Bergman,
Waiting for Bogie and Claude Rains
To walk off together in the fog.
Beginning of a beautiful friendship.
Figures move in black, gray, and white.
Cats scream and my finger is bleeding;
"Some heavy thing fell on it,"
I explain. "I think it's broken."
Across the hall a girl is dragging
A dirty mattress up the stairs and she's crying.
Now is the hour when I am set up,
Clamped between leather-covered bookends,
Cold linoleum next to my naked face, my naked body,
Dodging beams from some official flashlight.
My rights are explained and some time later,
I am asked to make a statement over tea.
Every knock on the red and yellow door
Is accompanied by a warm uniformed voice.
Dirty socks in the armchair, dirty books on my desk.
Rushing to put my clothes on again.
Someone asks, pointing, "Who's the man in the photograph?"
"Oh," I answer, dusting the frame, "William Faulkner."
Are explanations necessary? Perhaps.
But I can hear helicopters whirling
Through this cold, rainy, October night.
Someone was beaten in the alley,
A crowd is gathering, laughing, shouting,
And my finger is still bleeding.
With one hand I squeeze and roll between my fingers
The loose fat flesh of my thigh, touch
Icy feet one against the other.

Someone asks, "Would it help, do you think,
                                        if I made some pudding?"
I laugh and lick the blood from my finger.

W. P. Kinsella

CARAWAY

Volume 3, Numbers 1 & 2

> *...in some of the Northern tribes the caraway plant was believed to hold supernatural powers... the placing of the white bloom of the plant on the eyes of a dying or recently deceased person was believed to condemn the spirit to eternal fire....*
>
> —Tales of the Great Spirit, V. 2

I WAS ABOUT twelve the fall that Ruth Buffalo killed herself. One shot from the 22 gun her father, Joe Buffalo, kept in the back bedroom of their house was all it took.

Ruth was, I guess, the most smart Indian girl ever come from around our place. She was the only Indian kid around who didn't live on the reservation. They say there was a big stink by the white people when she went to their school instead of to the Indian Affairs school on the reserve. She got better marks than the white kids and the government end up paying her way clear through university because she so smart. She is study to be a teacher, and the kids who had her—she come back and teach us Indians at the reserve school even though she could have gone anywhere she wanted—say she is the best teacher they ever had. She can even speak our language and the kids in her class don't hate school as much as everybody else does.

But she killed herself anyway. What I hear from Joe Buffalo a lot later is she stay late to the school one night and something is happen to her on the way home. She is run into her house and scream and cry to her Papa that she been had by a farmer live across the field aways, Mr. Russell Bevans. Old Joe try to talk to her but she is gone crazy in her mind. "I be dirty forever, Papa," she say to him, "Forever and ever." And then she run to the bedroom and shoot herself.

Old Joe Buffalo he is no ordinary Indian. He is not a reserve Indian. He is own his own farm across the highway from the reservation. Old Joe, he is old enough to be around when reservations is made up and even way back then he is have so much pride he say he not take nothing he don't earn with his own hands. He bought the land so long ago nobody remembers how he got the money.

"I a funny old bugger," he used to say to me. "That's what the people in town say. They figure cause I old I don't hear. And they figure at the bank that cause I can't write my name I can't count. Them girls try lots of times give me less than I should have." Joe is too old to farm no more but he rents his land and gets paid for it.

Nobody like Old Joe much. The reserve Indians don't like that he don't be like them: do nothing, and the white people sure not like it when he thinks he can be the same as them. That's what the white people think . . . Old Joe, the last thing he ever wants to do is be white.

Everybody wonder about him some and like most kids I wonder too. When I about 10 me and my friend Frank Fencepost go sneaking around his place. We crawl down from the highway on our bellies and make pretend we are tracking buffalo and that make it a big joke to us.

We crawl right up to the back of the house and boy we is some proud of ourself, when all of a sudden I feel something cold on the back of my neck, and there is Old Joe Buffalo with his shot gun. I don't know how he got there . . . I never hear nothing.

Frank he see what happened to me and he break and run. Old Joe turn and fire the shot gun at Frank, but I see he shoot way up in the trees make sure he don't hit him. Frank he yell like he been hit anyway and run until we hear him hit Old Joe's barbed wire fence really hard.

"What you do sneak around like a thief?" he say.

"We don't mean nothing. We play at track buffalo."

Old Joe smile a little on me. "You just been caught by oldest Buffalo in this part of country," he say, and I look at him and see that his face is all brown and wrinkled up like Eathen Firstrider's hand tooled chaps. "Who are you?" he asks.

"Silas Ermineskin," I say. For some reason I don't know I not scared of him at all.

"You never do nothing but scare away game wearing white man's shoes," and he look at my running shoes with my toes hang out. "Soft as moss," he say, and point at his own moccasins. "If you drink tea, Silas Ermineskin, you can come in my cabin."

He got on an old red and black mackinaw that he wear everyday for years. His face all wrinkled up but his eyes clear and shiny like a little kid's. His pipe poke out of his mackinaw pocket, and that what his house smell like, his pipe. He don't smoke tobacco but bunch of leaves and roots he collect himself. All the furniture in the house Old Joe made himself is what he tells me.

"You like to learn track game like real Indian?" he ask me.

"Sure I would," I say. "And do ceremony dances and make mean face with war paint. Could you learn me that too?"

"If you want I teach you." He pour us out tea that he cook in a tin pan on the woodstove. He tell me some stories then about when he was a boy and there hardly any whitemen in our country and it not even called Alberta then. And he tell me about his daughter and how proud he is of her going to graduate the university that year. Old Joe tell me he was 70 when Ruth born and already work on his third wife who was only 20 or so. When Ruth is about 2 her and her Momma take the measles and the Momma is die. I count in my head and figure that he is most 95 years old.

"I hear your family coming to look for you," he says then. I forgot all about Frank and how I been there all day already.

"I don't hear nothing," I say.

"Be quiet! Be still as a post and stretch your ears out."

I don't hear nothing even when I stretch my ears, but in a few minutes my Pa, Sam Standing-by-the-door, Frank and some other kids is come through the trees. Pa is carrying his rifle.

They is happy to see me o.k. but my Pa tells me, "Silas, don't you never go back there. He's crazy old man thinks he too good for us Indians." So of course I went back every time I got a chance.

Old Joe he don't read or write but he is look around him and understand lots. He say us Indians got to go forward or backward. Our people is gonna die, he say, if we sit still like we do now on the reserves.

"Look at our women," he used to say. "They don't like be called squaw no more. They drink beer, ride around in whiteman's cars. Our women the most proud and feared anywhere around at one time. It hurt my heart to see them now. And the men sit around all day curse the whiteman with one hand take his money with the other."

I think of Chief Tom Crow-eye who is most of the time wear a suit and go to meetings in Edmonton and Calgary. Yet nothing ever change for us.

Old Joe and me get to be great friends. I spend a lot of time there and he tell me the stories his Mama used to tell him about how the Great Spirit make the land and the people and all that.

"I get signed up by the missionaries long time ago," he say like he don't feel quite right about it. "I do it for my old squaw. She is want to believe in whiteman's God so I say o.k. The church people say we got to believe only their way and forget ours. So I never be what they call a religious man. Ruth, she's good catholic. Go to church three times on Sunday. I'd rather lay out muskrat traps."

We is all, most of us Indians, catholic. A long time ago the missionaries come around get everybody join up the church though most people don't understand what it is all about.

Somebody asks us what religion we are, we say, "Catholic, . . . I guess."

Even when Ruth come home to teach I hardly ever see her. She is always stay late to the school or work sometimes for the church.

Then come the time Ruth is kill herself. Poor Old Joe, it sure hurts him to be an Indian then. He walk to the store at Hobbema Crossing and call the R.C.M.P. but they take 4-5 hours before they come. Old Joe tell them what happened but they don't hardly listen to him, he says.

"I tell them it Russell Bevans done it, but they just makes faces to each other like I don't know anything," he tells me.

Russell Bevans he look like a giant to me, then. I guess he was six foot or so with big wide shoulders and a head like a basketball with thin red hair on top. His eyes was pale blue and close together like a pig. His hands make five or six of mine, big like baseball gloves with big black fingernails. He chew snuff, "snoose" he called it, and it was what you smell about him when he come close to you. Everybody know he been after Indian girls lots of times before. Some he get, some he don't. Some older girls go with him for maybe $5 after they been to town drinking.

The R.C.M.P. guys talk to Russell Bevans. He say he don't know nothing about Ruth, and his wife, a scared little white lady with grey hair, say he been home in the yard all that day, and his son say so too, he is about 14, fat, like to beat up Indian kids, and got the same pig face as his Pa.

Nobody ever thought to have a doctor look at Ruth. She is just an Indian.

In town I hear ladies talk in the Co-op store.

"That Ruth was kind of an uppity one," they say. "And kind of strange like her father. She was probably up to no good of some kind. Had something to hide."

"I bet," said another one, "that if they checked her out they'd find she was pregnant. Indian girls are all like that. And imagine her accusing Russell, why he'd give you the shirt off his back, and he hasn't missed church in ten years."

The worst for Old Joe is when the priests from the church say that Ruth can't be buried in the church grave yard because she kill herself. Old Joe swear that everything he say is true. He swear it to the R.C.M.P., the priests, and to me. But I the only one who believe him.

"It not matter to me," he say, "but she care plenty about it. Her spirit not rest unless she can be buried there." But it don't matter what he say the church don't change its mind.

Joe is build a coffin for Ruth himself. I never feel more sorry for anyone than him that day. He is just an old man who don't hardly speak the whiteman language and don't understand why nobody do nothing for his daughter.

He hires two Indians, Rufus Fire-in-the-draw, and Charlie Blanket, to tear down a granary that he don't use no more and pile the boards up against his corral fence. Then he have them put the coffin on top of the boards and he is set fire to all of it. He had went to the church and ask the priests come down and two of them do.

The sun is going down and a storm is blow big clouds across the sky. The fire roars like wind as it burn up against the dark. Old Joe Buffalo is kneel down in the corral, raise his arms to the sky and cry the death song of our people like it been taught to him most a hundred years ago. Charlie and Rufus don't know what to do as they stand by the back of the corral and they finally must sneak away. The priests twist the beads around their necks and the fire flash on their silver crosses and long black robes. After a while they go away making lots of the sign of the cross. The fire burn down and all I can hear is the voice of Old Joe Buffalo crying out his sorrow in the fall night.

"I glad you stay, Silas," he say to me when he finally stop. "I going to do something tonight and I don't like to be alone at it."

He bring from the house a Roger's Golden Syrup can and we go back to the fire. There is just a few ashes glow a bit like eyes in the dark. Old Joe fills the can up with ashes—if the coals hurt his hands he don't ever show it—and then we walk the long miles up the highway to the catholic church cemetery and Old Joe is bury that can of ashes there in the graveyard. Then we go back and he makes tea for us. He don't ask me to but I sleep at his house that night.

All that winter I spend a lot of time at Old Joe's. He learns me how to make war paint and how to set snares and he tells me the legends of our people that almost been forgot by everybody.

"Violets is soft like women's faces," he say, "put violets on a grave and you make the spirit happy."

And he tell me about caraway. I even find that one in a book one time and I print it out at the start of my story so everybody is know Old Joe is tell me the truth.

In the spring he spend a lot of time track Russell Bevans. He get to know where he go every day and what he do. When Bevans is work in his fields Old Joe and sometimes me too, is never far away, but Russell Bevans he never know that. I wonder what it is Old Joe going to do.

In the middle of the summer I come down to Old Joe's place early one morning. Sneak up real quiet like he's taught me to do—Joe is even make for me my own moccasins—and peek through the window. There is Old Joe at the table, naked from the waist up, look in his little square mirror propped on the table and put war paint on his skinny old chest. Then on his face with red, yellow and blue colour is make himself fierce and scary.

Then he put on his mackinaw and go off across the fields to where his land join up with Russell Bevan's land. Russell have a private road run along there and he been hauling hay along there with a hay-rack and his tractor the last couple of days. I follow way behind so he don't know that I there.

Old Joe gets down in the ditch in the water and waits for the tractor to come along. When it get to maybe fifty feet from where he is, Old Joe takes off his mackinaw and rise up out of the ditch like a spirit himself.

Russell Bevans have to either hit Old Joe or turn the wheel. What Old Joe count on I guess is that Russell just be scared and turn the tractor cause I bet he sure like to run over an Indian. He turns the wheel and the tractor tip right over. He make a half try to jump clear but he is too big for that. The tractor is on top of him in the slough water before he know it. He yell some and try to get loose but he is pinned by his chest, hurt a lot and can hardly keep his head above the green water.

"Go get help, you crazy old bastard," he yells at Joe. But Joe is stand look down at him and maybe smile a little. I crawl silent until I right across the road. I lay in the water with the bull rushes and peek across.

"You tell me the truth about my girl," Old Joe says after a while.

"I don't know nothing," says Russell Bevans, the green water right up to his mouth. "Help me!"

"First you tell the truth. I don't go for help until."

Russell Bevans, he swear and yell. Then he beg Old Joe some to help him. Russell have lots of pain and after a while he make a funny noise and pass out. His head goes under water, but Old Joe wade right in and lift up his head so he don't drown. Then from the pocket of his jeans he take out some caraway flowers and place on each of Russell Bevans' eyes. He cradle his head like a baby until he wake up. Two or three times this happen until Russell Bevans is finally tell Old Joe, yes I hurt your daughter. I sorry I done it. If you get me help I'll even tell the R.C.M.P. that I done it.

Old Joe Buffalo is smile just a touch and the next time Russell Bevans is pass out Joe don't grab his head. He scatters the last of the caraway flowers on the water above his face and I hear the bubles come up through the water around them.

Joe goes get his mackinaw and walk real slow away.

"You can walk with me, Silas," he say to me.

"How you know I there," I say. "I walk real quiet."

"You walk like two moose chased by a wolf. I hear you ever since you crossed the highway."

Gary Pacernick

PORTRAIT

Volume 3, Numbers 1 & 2

As his father holds his hand,
This small boy stands on a wicker chair
Kneeling slightly,
His head tilted forward
Almost level with his father's head.
At their backs are elm trees, sunlight,
That white chevy parked in the garage.
Awaiting the camera's flash, they smile.
Their shadows lengthen on the grass.

Margherita Woods Faulkner

THE BEEHIVE

Volume 3, Numbers 1 & 2

Among a honeycomb of lockers
students and staff pass each other.
Throughout the day a flat buzz
releases them, then sucks them back
into fluorescent rooms and offices.

Janitors come in the afternoon
as the swarm subsides.
They sprinkle the floors with cleaning powder
as though its sweet smell
could be of some use to the hive.

Hugh Fox

51

Volume 3, Numbers 1 & 2

New Year's Day night, 42nd and Broadway, two Dead drifting along, grab around a lamppost.

"Some wind."

"You said it."

"I'm Mahmud."

"I'm Hennig Brand."

"One time I had fifty thousand people killed in one day, and I burnt the temple at Mathura to the ground after I'd plundered its jewel-encrusted gold statues. . . ."

"I isolated phosphorus from human piss."

A gust of wind tore them from their lamppost and as Mahmud blew across Times Square he tried to remember the other guy's name—and what *is* phosphorus . . . ?

Richard Morris

THE PEARLY GATES

Volume 3, Numbers 1 & 2

Humphrey Bogart stands before the Pearly Gates. A **Choir of Angels** is singing somewhere. Slowly, the Gates open, revealing St. Peter, who is **Peter Lorre.**

Peter Lorre: I bet you have more respect for me now.

Slowly and majestically, God strides forward. God is **Sidney Greenstreet.** The **Choir of Angels** is singing His praises. He starts to say something, but He can't be heard; the **Angels** are making too much noise. He motions to them to be quiet, then turns back to **Bogart.**

Sidney Greenstreet: This isn't what you expected, is it, motherfucker?

Pat Dooley / 73% of original / Volume 2, Numbers 2 & 3

$3.50
The Actualist Anthology
Edited by Morty Sklar & Darrell Gray
The Spirit That Moves Us Press

Anselm Hollo

SONG OF THE TUSK

The Actualist Anthology

the elephant
        bogged down
thousands of years ago

the fragmentary tusk
        now in a glass case

no no those are untrue statements
it is I
        am in the glass case
                counting
                        the stubs of museum tickets

it is the elephant
        walks the downs
                laughs at the sea
                        growling

there is no such thing
        as thousands of years
I drop a stone on your head
        from the elephant's back

show me
        show me the thousands of years

I walk through the water
        throwing stones at the women
                on the beach
        the honeymoon women
                their eyes far apart

frightened
        they close the glass case
        over themselves & their lovers
for thousands of years

Oh Goofy,
tapdancing in the kitchen
in the moonlight
of streetlight
Oh dripping faucet
song of environmental unconcern
beauty of waste
we sing

Oh Coney Island
thrill of dying
25 cents by the ocean
laughing entrance to Fear
a dozen clams on the halfshell

Oh salt air, hot sauce

Oh my
Daffy Duck saltwater taffy
3 shots for a quarter
Oh sweet rag doll reward
Midnight in Flatbush
Oh closing of the eternally open steeplechase
trashy windy blacktops of the sauerkraut mustard
cotton candy night

Oh Light

Oh subway home
Oh home
Star Travellers of Brooklyn
Moonlight on the oil slick
Oh Mark Twain

of the green condom river,
Ellis Island ghosts
Liberty

Oh say
can you see

David Hilton

I TRY TO TURN IN MY JOCK

The Actualist Anthology

Going up for the jump-shot,
Giving the kid the head-fakes and all
'Til he's juked right out the door of the gym
And I'm free at the top with the ball and my touch,
Lofting the arc off my fingertips,
I feel my left calf turn to stone
And my ankle warp inward to form when I land
A neat right angle with my leg,
And I'm on the floor,
A pile of sweat and sick muscles,
Saying,
Hilton,
You're 29, getting fat,
Can't drive to your right anymore,
You can think of better things to do
On Saturday afternoons than be a chump
For a bunch of sophomore third-stringers–
Join the Y, steam and martinis and muscletone,
But, shit,
The shot goes in.

Chuck Miller

REQUIEM: A SURREALIST GRAVEYARD

The Actualist Anthology

there was Nadja's glove flickering somewhere
under the Madza bulb
which i think of now and then
an imaginary semi-transparent thing lost somehow
in what we could call a quantum of our love
a space-time geometry with its coordinate seam
unzipped onto the void,
does the void collect our mad love
surely the only kind which could exist
like a soft blue grave yard
upsidedown in a telescope eye
clasping us with the love of its ether arms
poor Mickelson-Morley trying to prove ether love with
mirrors,
mirrors we can only disappear into with Huertibus
their love too fathomless for our mortal dimensions
but the ether wind spills down sometimes
wetting our seared black cheeks
and we realize it must be the kindly blue grave yard,
or is someone basting the earth in silence?
a great baked apple stewing in space
the gigantic spoon up-lifted
i hear silence running over the curve of the sky
but there is something i have lost
which we all wore then, remember comrades?
the good luck glove
i have lost the good luck glove
it kept me going in this rain of sad asteroids
i have lost the good luck glove
my hand like a socket in space
wanders already on that journey to another star

Steve Toth

SYMBOLS

The Actualist Anthology

Things are born out of ideas.
The mind of man gets an identity from each experience,
Consequently nothing touches our attentions
Which is left unexplained to some part of us.
Where the same things are not available
They are grown in the fertile human mind.
Thus the savage has an explanation
For every experience in his world of phenomena,
And the same things shape themselves in our minds.
But just how is this accomplished?
Men and women look out
Upon anything that rises spontaneously.
What they see is far closer to depicting
What they are thinking about
Than any other symbol which they could later devise
To mean the same thing.

Cinda Kornblum

THE HONEYMOONERS

The Actualist Anthology

When a youngster
I thought they were saying "celery"
not salary.
The green crisp stuff
somehow a focus of the grown-up world.
My father didn't have a
salary: he had a farm.
And just as I wondered what city folks
did with their garbage if they had no pigs
I wondered why wives nagged their husbands
to ask the boss for more celery.

College years solved the celery question.
Along with the mayonnaise & ketchup
celery was the only food still in the refrigerator
at the end of the month.

Allan Kornblum

HER HAIR IS WET

And behold the bee of sleep
At the umbrella's tip
—Reverdy

The soft lips of the heat register
Open, breathe, and above it particles of air
Solidify into furniture.
For no reason, you feel as if you should
Know the young girl in the zebra striped coat
Sitting on the newly formed and hovering davenport
And you start to say . . . .
But she interrupts. My hair is wet, I hope
The plush of this divan isn't being ruined
I'd best walk around
I came in to get out of the rain.
You take her hand and lead her into the yellow kitchen.
Taffeta curtains are stuffed in a vase on the table
Violets and grapes frame the windows
With the beginning and end of summer
Il pleut, she turns from the window eating a grape
Il pleut, she says again
And takes the memory of coffee you offer

Jim Mulac

ELEGY FOR DUKE ELLINGTON

The Actualist Anthology

The more you know, the more there is;
the more music you get into, the more you want.
—Duke Ellington

Like sweet brother Johnny Hodges dying alone
in a bathroom during the band's intermission,
the Duke became as cool as he ever wanted to be.
In the spring of 1973 I saw him in Iowa City:
74 years old, the loud snapping crack
of his finger & thumb, he was an old
man lanky as an iron tree, discreet when
he socked the machine of his hips, once
elegant and now with long, wavy grey hair
—loose and casual on his extended vacation.
Duke Ellington made a career of freedom,
"getting paid to do what you love to do."
More articulate than leaders of his world, he
could look at the keyboard & see again how easy
it would be to make a sound so beautiful anybody
everywhere would know how madly he loved us.

John Sjoberg

WE TRY NOT TO TOUCH SO CLOSE

The Actualist Anthology

We try not to touch so close to our hearts,
But the night's unavoidable mind has made us
Try to bind our lives with
Strings we cannot find.
Its deep placed calls of softness
Draw our threadful thoughts
To hearts that are not there.
This compelling conversation avoids
The definition of our indispensable sighs.
This silence is all we need. We hear
The heart of love, and wait to see
Its daylight dawning, and stay the day into eternity.

Darrell Gray

AN OLD SOUTHERN CRITIC TAKES A LOOK AT MY POEMS

The Actualist Anthology

grasshoppers, wheelchairs, rosebuds!
all those variably cloudy images

bundled up & flung at the reader as if
communication depended on an alien plug, a verbal

fire-sale, syntax slashed to the bone
& what's more we haven't the slightest

buried symbol or submerged meaning
to hold on to—total mayhem—"with this kind

of aesthetic how does he tie
his shoelaces is what I want to know"

not to mention all those dim & unemphasized
figments that flash across the page

all those parking lots preposterous similies
"the stars like tiny lawnchairs in the sky"

where did the soul go
to drag these fugitive embers from its fire

and was there a first fire, a fire fashioned
after no other, a fire of the final mind

from which we emerge like schoolboys in a dream
to bone white rivers & the fear of owls . . .

Say something deep, like the fear of rivers, something
pure & lean we can teach our kids

the lyric is a flexible form, I know:
birds, beasts and animals

in season sing their blunt reciprocal praises.
Mimeo machines murmur. Though that might be a

variable measure, all variance decrees
a cosmic tedium—"dialectic" we call it: nude idiom

of the thing reborn. The gentle researcher
tilts to the modular pinkness of the snow—

an erudite boy, addicted to spiral notebooks,
yoga, and the oblique "come-on" of dark girls

.... These old eyes grow older with each word,
& Ambiguity, like a pregnant queen, rules

the landscape where I sit. Ripe berries hang in tangles
over Samuel Johnson's grave—"like ornaments of indecision",

you might say .... And yet, there is an occasional
brilliant twist. I quote one poem, BAFFLING TURNS, in toto:

Asleep at 60 mph. No doubt the poet here has in mind
how much eludes him. Or, as Allen Tate succinctly said:

"For where Time rears its muted head and all appalls
We know not where we stand nor where we fall."

Anonymous / Morty Sklar & Grandma Rose / Volume 1, Number 1

Sheila Heldenbrand

"THERE IS A LITTLE HOUSE"

Volume 1, Number 1

There is a little house.
Inside is an old woman.
Someone says:
The good eye projects,
the evil eye attracts light.
She has a good eye.
She has white hair.
My innermost fears
come popping out of her mouth.
She jumps onto the running board
of the red ford truck,
and whispers in the window
in my ear, "Don't worry
you're going to be happy now."

Catherine Doty

NITROUS OXIDE

Volume 1, Number 1

The hiss of gas became a steady thump
and the smell went away.
You did not yet exist.

The poor get their teeth repaired
at twenty-five.
Our parents don't wait
with wires and tools,
can't wait with the proper bribes.
We get what's left slapped together–
bleed on our bibs.

I open my eyes, sure the room
will fade to green,
the tubes all bloom.
I know you hear me call
through the bloody gauze.
You are on your way–
perhaps you've stopped for flowers.

Then, in the mirror, the gaps–
the pits of neglect.
All these losses!
You turn and tap-dance home.

Attila Jozsef

DUSK

Volume 1, Number 1

This sharp clear dusk was made for me.
Constructions of bare branches
gracefully support the empty air.
The self, made subject, separates from the world,
becomes self-absorbed, perhaps destroyed.
Who knows? My intuition could give the answer,
but like a dog scolded by its master,
it wanders morosely in the cold yard,
howling at strangers. Without it, I am helpless.
Only one thing is certain here—what's wrong.
It's good that lambs still exist: they're something
to clutch at. This is how a child learns to walk;
only I can't be a child, because I am too
fretful, stubborn, treacherous.
Could everyone be just as sly and
obstinate? Perhaps. I wouldn't know.
One winks at me and says, "Nice guy,"
another, "Lazy slob, you're not working again,
but your belly's full, you make sure of that."
(I guess I shouldn't.) Another shoves money at me,
"Be happy, I understand, I went through the same
things."
I'm thrown around, handled, croaked at, jostled,
but no one notices my hunchback.
I carry it like a crazy mother her big belly,
out of which, she thinks, she'll give birth
to silence or pure emptiness.

—translated from the Magyar by John Batki

Nikolai Gumilev

THE SIXTH SENSE

Volume 1, Number 1

How fine is the wine that loves us,
and the wholesome bread offering itself
to the oven for our sake,
and the woman who allows us to love her
after she's tried us to her heart's full.

But what are we to make
of a pumpkin sunset
over a sky that's growing colder, more silent
and more terribly calm?
What are we to make of deathless poems . . . ?

You can't eat, or drink, or kiss them . . .
The moment flies apart
though we wring it in our hands,
and parts of ourselves pass
each other, like strangers, without nodding.

Like a boy distracted from his game stares
at the bathing girls,
and though knowing nothing of love—
like a waterdrop sizzling on hot metal—
he boils on a pinpoint of desire;

just as in earliest mud-time
the slimy amphibian, feeling
under its hide the aching back-buds
of wings teething skyward,
squealed with impotence caught in thickets,

so, age after age—how long, Lord?—
under the revolving knives of nature and art
our spirit cries out,
the flesh shrivels,
as they sweat to bring an organ
of the sixth sense to birth.

—adapted from the Russian by Jack Marshall

Audrey Teeter

STEER WRESTLING

Volume 1, Number 1

the man strides the horse in the gate
the steer waits
then it all begins
the run
the chase
the fall from the saddle
the grasp of the horns
"what is my body worth?" thinks the
        cowboy
"I don't know" says the bull
as he lays himself down

Madeleine Keller

ANCESTRIA

Volume 1, Number 1

I come from women who worked in fields
who walked through wilderness
(rifles on their hips
I come from women with tyrannical fathers and 10 children
with wombs barren as the desert
committed to marriage
who never knew men
I come from women who died too early
with no dreams and manicured hands
whose life was waiting
I come from women who admired diamonds in store windows
who steal food and clothing
I come from women with small breasts and large hips
with perfect teeth
who starved and refused war
who could not read
who never learned to speak
who beat their children
I come from women in dreams, factories, mines, ghettoes,
strange countries of wealth
ashamed of sex and speaking
I come from women in housedresses and high heels
unable to laugh
who had to die to survive

I come from women
to womanhood

I do not know my mother's face
but now I see her everywhere

Dave Morice

IN THE MIDDLE OF A WIND TUNNEL

Volume 4, Numbers 2 & 3

And here we are in the middle of a wind tunnel
in which the wind has been turned off
for us to see exactly where the wind
goes in and where it goes out

And here's the ON OFF button that turns the wind
on and off, of course, and we don't turn it ON
until we're OUT, and we watch the fans
and bellows generate enough energy

And here's the middle of the generator
where the power for the wind is stored
when the wind isn't being used.
Sir, don't press that ON button.

And now we'll leave the tunnel because very soon
the owners will want to turn the wind on
and watch things blow from one end of the tunnel
to the other and back again.

Stuart Mead / 30% of original / Volume 4, Numbers 2 & 3

Constantin Toiu

Chapter 9 of

THE GALLERY OF WILD IVORY

Volume 4, Numbers 2 & 3

IT WAS mid-November 1957, and it had been a cold night of storm and rain. I had been sleeping in my wheelchair on the wooden gallery, half hidden in the ivy, wrapt in a warm blanket. Nights were getting longer and longer, and the just balance between light and darkness had struck me as being ephemeral, like everything else. Dead and old leaves rustled in my sleep. As morning approached, I forced my eyes closed several times, trying to go back to the shelter within myself, like a beast in its den, looking up at the dark, starry sky.

I had made my mind up to wake, at last. I kept my eyes wide open in the cold morning darkness. I remembered Chiril, a character always to be mentioned in the third person, whose place can be taken by anyone. Chiril, who was gone to be alive again, sometime, in who knows what other sparkling heresy in the world.

I had wheeled my chair closer to the wall. I was ready to start another day and spend it like the cripple I am, in compulsory immobility.

I waited for the sun to rise. Or perhaps it wouldn't rise at all.

My neighbors would one by one turn up on the gallery. Grandfather, whose nights were always short. The mayor, a hero of two wars who had once entered on horseback Frau Bertha's cakeshop on Calarasi Street and had thus inspected the white tables at which the seated people were enjoying the best *kremschnitt* in the city. He had named his white cat Rosemarie after a girl he used to know at Frau Bertha's place. Then his son, who had fought in one war, the war we mention as the last one.

We'll sip coffees, eat cherry jam, and chat. I'll have to tell them my dreams, for nothing ever happens to me, except in dreams. When it rains, we dream about drowned people. I had dreamt of the good friend of my childhood, Sterica, who had drowned long ago. Sterica was drowning in the river, and I was madly running towards the village for help, but the road was barred by the twenty-seven black oil tanks of a train crossing the fields. Sterica had won a bet; that he could remain under water as long as you counted a hundred.

Grandfather's son was a Professor who had been giving lectures on the Strength of Materials at the Polytechnic Institute. He was retired now and was teaching me everyday.

"Good morning," he said. I was in high spirits and I answered back in the Gypsies' language, which I had learned as a child. I enjoyed the old Sanskrit taste of this language, like the salt, dead and heavy, on the shores of Asia, haunted by famine and rough winds.

"Te traizem but bers fericime—Many happy years to you."

Other times I would say: *"Sucar araclemtume sastereste"*—meaning, "I am happy to find you in good health," although it did not suit me, since I never came from anywhere. It was always others who came from some other place and found me always in the same, and they revolved around me, like round some burnt-out dwarf star of a formidable density, whose huge mass had already turned into lead.

I knew what I was going to get, a new lecture on the strength of materials. I submitted myself to that. He had been in prison, and his pleasure to talk had increased enormously. In fact, he had talked a lot during those seven years in prison, so his fluency had been subject to a kind of acceleration.

I pretended to listen to him, while my thoughts were wandering; I felt like those ladies who go to the concert and whose voices can be heard in the sudden interval between the *andante* and the *allegro ma non troppo*, in the dignified silence floating for several seconds over the hall: "First, my dear, you have to beat the eggs . . ."

"I suppose you are clear about the three Sigmas." I was stone cold, I nodded approval.

"First we have 'Sigma of Proportionality.' In this case, the distortions brought about by the effect are elastic. Then we have 'Sigma of Flowing'—the material is distorted under the effort. Then we have the most interesting case, 'Sigma of Breaking,' when the strength of matter acquires a human, stoic courage. It is the moment when the steel gives way, after it gets tough and strong in a supreme effort, like that of people before they die. It is that sudden lucid moment of conscience, when you remember all of your life, and it is strange to notice how an inorganic material can behave—like some living flesh. The man-made material seems to have borrowed man's character, as if they shared the same fate, according to the same laws that govern matter and spirit alike."

I turned my head and looked at him. I admitted I was attracted by this theory of his, associating matter with someone who has to take a lot, who puts up with too much, who has to patiently endure beyond some implicit limit of human patience.

Like the iron bridge on which troops should never march and keep in step. On the contrary, they must pretend they are having a walk, and even walk on tiptoe, for they have to try and deceive the resistance beneath their feet, since the material of the bridge is determined to give way and break if subjected to a rhythm too mechanically and brutally insistent, or lasting for too long a time. Since such a rhythm is not known to the natural universe, a man too cannot take too much of that rhythmical pressure, mechanically and stupidly repeatedly upon him, upon the same already weakened point. Well, that man falls dead when you least expect it. A man can behave like the bridge which suddenly breaks when the soldiers are merrily singing and marching on it, the bridge won't stand this lack of subtlety and finesse anymore, the bridge is no longer willing to listen to the troops: "A fair, sweet, and darling chickie . . ." The bridge has a sudden wish to break into two, a sudden desire to no longer be a bridge between two banks. Destiny is like a commanding officer, who treads on us in a rhythm of his own, and marches on, upright and haughty. But our backs, I tell you, they also have their own laws, like metal, and they will no more want to be a bridge, a bridge of blood and flesh for those heavy, gigantic steps to step down upon.

Perhaps these are the moral consequences of the great

equations discovered by brilliant minds, whose names and dates I had come to learn by heart.

Hooke, 1703. Bernoulli, 1705. Navier, 1836. Poisson, 1840. Castigliano, 1800.

I suddenly remembered the pond, a meander of the river where the Gypsies were allowed to bathe, and Gioca the Gypsy-woman who had taught me love in the dark cellar on the Thursday night of her daughter's wedding; she had nursed me once, but still, on that wedding night, I was her white and eager master.

"In my time . . ." the old men said, and whatever had never really happened had a place in their minds. I shall also tell stories about "my time." But my earliest time was the train dragging its oil-tanks when Sterica got drowned, whose face is Chiril's now, sometimes, in dreams. We were bathing in the River Sarata, deep down in its swollen belly, the water came to our mouths and the sand was running under our feet and the streams took us to the Gypsies' Place, the spot, chosen or reserved for them, from where we could watch the naked gypsy-women also bathing. In their spot, the water was spoilt by narrow traces of oil and by the blood-stream flowing from the slaughter-house nearby.

The sons of India were cornered and compelled to bathe in this spot, pushed there to the brink of squalor and filthy death. The Mayor had turned that wooden building, once a summer garden, into a slaughter-house, which he had endowed with a cement floor, sinks, pegs for skins, a grindstone and water taps. He had proudly exclaimed, in his inauguration speech, when they had adorned the slaughter-house with green fir branches: "You see, gentlemen, anything can turn into anything."

The bellowing of the oxen never ceased, they were brought there to be hit in the head by Barabulea, the son of the famous gypsy musician who used to play the bass at weddings and parties.

At his own wedding with Gioca's daughter, I'd made a bet—that I had the guts to get into the cellar full of drunken gypsies. I had won this bet, indeed, but two days later Sterica had won his bet, that he was able to keep his breath under water as long as you counted a hundred. He had kept his breath longer than that, to the point where his perpetual life began. The drunken town imbecile had jumped into the river to save his life, and they both drowned while I was running in the wrong direction crying, "Help, help!" But the train was barring the road and I lost my bearings, and instead of coming nearer the village, I was getting farther and farther away from it.

Our teacher labelled me a traitor.

The two corpses burnt in the church, the fire started quickly from the candles and spread to the paper wreaths, and destroyed the bodies of my friend and his would-be saviour, burned at the stake of eternal regrets. So when the priest came and unlocked the church door, when the funeral gathered a crowd of people, there were two caskets of ashes lying in the coffins, as if the test of water, having not been enough, had to be completed with a test of fire. Several days before, Sterica and me had both been present at the gypsies' wedding; the fiddler's son had given us a warm welcome, his black hair was parted in the middle and the grease that was shining there reminded me of a rifle on a gun-rack.

He wore black patent leather shoes that had never been his, and were probably pinching everywhere, for at every step he had to bite his thick violet-blue lips. Later on that night, he took his shoes off and walked about in white cotton socks. He wore an old worn-out, tight coat, that had belonged to his father the famous fiddler, about whom every gypsy musician in the town was proud, since the old man had been hired at the casino in Sinaia several winters running.

Yes, I had a warm spot in my heart for gypsies, but I could not attach any meaning to that. The married women were eating pumpkin seeds, and they instructed the bride about what was going to happen to her; Rusca, Gioaca's daughter, was only fifteen, and she cleaned and white-washed houses, autumns and springs.

At sixteen, her mother had been the glory of the garrison. She had accompanied her first lover, a good looking young officer, to a party where she had danced naked on the table. They had named her "Black Gioconda," and Gioaca was a fragment of that glorious name, which had been left to her like a souvenir, a broken piece of a once precious jewel. The girl had danced naked on the table, but wore the officer's cap on her head. As a reward, he took her up in the Headquarters' balloon, he bribed the sentinel away, and they flew over the town and saw the fields, the winding river flowing into vineyards, and the railroad—an extraordinary experience high up in the sky, something no one had ever lived before, and she could never forget. She still speaks about it, if she is still alive.

Gioaca played an important role in the amorous life of the town, she was the first lady of a secret brothel hidden behind the barber's shop. The place was teeming with young, smart and wasteful officers. Napoleon in an oil painting hung on the wall, he was the barber's idol, but the officers said he was a ladies' man and nothing more. The officers had turned the barber's shop into an attractive and brilliant place. Ostensibly, they came for shaves and haircuts. A red curtain led directly to the clandestine brothel. The great adventure of Gioaca's youth had proliferated a harem of seeds-eating gypsy girls. In summertime, they were sitting and waiting outside in the tiny garden, under the shady mulberry tree. The freshly shaven customer would go into the yard and look, and utter a name, or point at the girl, if he didn't know her by name. The gypsy girl would rise to her feet and join him in the adjoining room. The man locked the door, and then everybody in the barber's shop was silent, trying to listen to what was happening behind the door.

Times had changed, the barber was dead before Gioaca's daughter grew up.

Rusca, the bride, was one year older than myself. She wore a white veil and a white lace blouse, my mother's presents to her.

I was fond of Rusca, we'd grown up together, and her mother had nursed me once, so we were like brother and sister. We had even secretly married, two years before her own wedding, in the darkness of a henhouse, where she'd lured me, voicelessly asking for my love. The cluck, cluck of the sleepy hens seemed to lure us away from the world of light. The hens even made room for us, as if they already understood everything that was going on, everything was clear to them from their point of view. Rusca lifted her dirty skirt and looked me in the eyes, waiting for me, saying nothing, her skirt was crumpled between her teeth and she only moaned. I took my trousers off and watched the terror with which she watched my naked belly, in her turn. I closed my eyes, when everything was too strong and no more under my control. I buried myself in her and in the world of cluck-clucks in the white-washed henhouse.

At the wedding, Sterica had dared me go down in the cellar of fallen gypsies. They were the people who could not dance on anymore, who were too tired or too weak to go on dancing round for hours and hours, and they were thrown out of the circle of gypsies, those who were still up and could still stand the effort.

Those who could still move after five hours of incessant *hora* dancing were fewer and fewer, so the circle of gypsies got smaller and smaller, but ever stronger at the same time; this was intentional, to approach the core of the tribe's real force. The law of the gypsy tribe was that this dance should point at the patient vigor of its people, revealed in the old, pure rhythm of an everlasting strength.

The weak, the fallen, were left out and thrown in the cellar where I was to go, too; I'd made this bet and meant to keep it. There were old people, women, children. "You go to sleep, all of you," the bridegroom had shouted at them.

I went downstairs and got used to the darkness in the cellar. Sleeping gypsies among wine barrels and things. Gioaca was talking to herself:

"*Of, prafos hai cic, of prafos hai cic pramende*—Oh, dust and mud, we are all under dust and mud."

She was down, tired after the wedding preparations and half drunk with brandy.

Gypsies had acquired the habit of drinking from us Romanians, but they were so good at it that, one could say, they were born addicted to it.

Gioaca saw me and called me to her. She smelt of tobacco, but I remembered her voice, the voice of the woman who had nursed me, and, drunk as she was, she wanted to nurse me now, forgetting I was no longer a baby, but a fourteen-year-old boy. I looked at her violet nipples, as she was getting ready to nurse me, her eyes were closed, and there was something on her face, despair, disgust or perhaps the paroxysm of expectation.

I went. Indeed. Her breasts smelt of smoke and ashes. She rocked me in her arms and, little by little, I woke up. It was like when you wake up at dawn and there is a long day in store for you. I could also hear again the clut-clut of the henhouse where I had loved Rusca.

After several days, it happened. The unavoidable penalty, the curse—that I was to spend the rest of my life in a wheelchair.

After Sterica's death it rained for a few days. I was at the window in my room, still thinking of my friend, of our raids together in the vegetable gardens.

Then, I saw Gioaca, crossing our street in the heavy rain. She had just come out of the pub and was carrying a bottle of rum. My nurse stumbled and fell in the middle of the road. The bottle broke, and the rum was spilt in the mud.

But she bent and started licking and sipping the rum that had been left in the mud, in a hole made by a horse-shoe. I felt I had a right to say no, I felt like her master who was ashamed of her; my own flesh and blood carried something of her own substance in my body, and I wanted her to be prouder, more dignified, more self-aware. I rose and climbed the windowsill and stood there ready to scold her. She looked at me and spoke to me and uttered words in the gypsy language, the words of her adoration for a young, white god. I was lost in the deep music of that voice, by that exciting old song which strangely contradicted her own mother tongue—so fit for quarrels and self-pitying lamentations. I moved as in sleep, when you know that nothing prevents you from flying. I was at the mezzanine storey, and I fell on my back, my spine hit the sidewalk paved with riverstones. My sentence was cruel and definite: immobility, the cripple I have been ever since.

—translated from the Romanian by Joana Grigorescu & Charles Clayton

Harley Elliott

THE IRIS

Volume 4, Numbers 2 & 3

for my father

The dream seems to say
I am saying goodbye
as I enter the door
of my father's old concern.
The secretaries sit in long
cool arrangements of powder and legs.
A single rain blue iris waits
at the corner of each desk

there is a gentle sorrow in the air

a gentle sorrow in my father
turning from his own dark room;
all the simple beauties he has
not allowed himself
to speak of   ever
rise upon his face

the sudden rainbow in the bathroom sink
he has seen in the
days of his life
the delicate yellow iris
growing under water at night

and my father is speaking at last
hands curving up like the
frangible hands of the iris
telling a story about
the blossoms that break
in the rain of years

and I am leaning over
my father at last
with the ease of a lover
presenting a lifetime of flowers.

Emilie Glen

SADLY OUT OVER

Volume 4, Numbers 2 & 3

Terror of lake,
Will it never leave me for minnows of light?
        Storm-dark lake
That choked out my Brother's life,
        My strong-swimmer Brother.
Mother's Mother long dead
        Came to Mama before the waters closed over,
Looking sadly out across the lake
        Where we were rowing,
                My big Brother and I

Terror of lake,
        My two-year-old runs off our Park path
                Into the woods,
Police Park men everyone searches,
        Worried over kidnapping molestation,
He could fall from glacial rocks

Tufted in sun innocence the lake,
Seeming harmless as its waterlilies,
        It is I who find him,
Blue-sandaled feet close to the water's edge,
        My Brother beside him,
                My Mother's Mother,
I storm down the hill to him,
        A small figure looking out on the lake

Jascha Kessler

RHADAMANTHYS

Volume 4, Numbers 2 & 3

OF ALL times for my car not to start. I'd be late for the last lecture. He had promised a summary discussion, touching on all that he had to teach us, including such problems as had heretofore resisted our reasonable formulation: such as, the source of judgment, the distribution of responsibilities between the logician of the left hemisphere and the esthete of the right hemisphere, and the unplumbed well of energy from which flows love and death in a single yet ambiguous stream labile in nature as time. Etcetera.

I had to roll the car down out of the driveway, after calling the garage for the towtruck. They came along and laid on the jump-cables in ten minutes, after which I drove there to have a hot charge put on the battery. That took half an hour more. Even so, I arrived only 50 minutes late . . . to find the others shuffling out. At the lectern stood Professor Freud, stacking examination booklets. I murmured an apology for my tardiness. I had not been late before in fact. He raised his eyebrows at me quizzically as I panted, winded from the three flights I had taken loping. My car wouldn't start, I said. He grunted, skeptical. As far as I was concerned, it was a likely story. I knew better than to insist on the truth. Instead, as was, I believe, my right, I simply asked him what was going on here.

In that low voice of his, that voice nearly a whisper, and which had caused us to lean forward tensely week after week just to catch his precise utterance, he observed simply that I was too late: "I have just given you your final examination."

But this was to be your last lecture, I protested. The exam's next week! "I am sorry for you," he shrugged. Sorry! How could you have done this! Whom does it serve! Time is needed in order to think! You promised to review all this matter in the end! "Yes, I have usually done so. Nevertheless, I decided to give the test today, and so finish things up for good." He indicated with a wave of his hand the questions written in small, italic script on the blackboard: with dark blue and bright yellow chalk. For a moment I studied them, uncomprehending. They seemed to be nonobjective statements about our life; they had nothing to do with the themes he'd discoursed upon all these many weeks. And who could have answered them in this one brief period we had? 50 minutes for essaying Process & Probability; Work, Waste, & Compensation; Appropriating Silence? And others too? I said, But surely, Professor, I can make it up? I'm perfectly willing to take a make-up exam whenever you wish to give it. "No, no," he whispered smiling, "now that you have seen my questions, it is impossible. I will never let you make it up. Too bad. However, I am sorry for you."

I stared at him as he grinned up at me through his crisp, salt and pepper beard. He did not flinch; but he did play for time, fumbling in his jacket pocket for a box of matches, averting his glance as he relit the soggy stump of his short, black Swiss cigar. I said nothing, because I knew there was nothing to be said now.

Still, I stood my ground: he'd have to pass around me to leave the room. Sucking at his cigar, he waited. He knew how to wait. I had to speak at last. So, I said, I've missed my chance. "Yes, well. You came late, you know." I beg your pardon? I said ironically. He did not reply. Keeping his eyes on me, knowing that I knew that what he taught was now mine in any case, and that he had committed the unforgivable, he gathered up the papers, that firm little man, tucked them beneath his arm, and came towards me.

Naturally I stepped aside. Nodding curtly once, he went out. It was all over. Resisting the rage that gathered in me, a force that seemed to rise from my toes, I drew a deep breath and held it for a few seconds. Then I turned and walked out into the vacant corridor. The Professor was striding towards the exit with that pace he'd learned on his Alpine walking holidays. As he passed through the door, he tossed the bundle of examination booklets into a trashbin. Then he was gone, a puff of thick Brasil tobacco smoke hanging in the air behind him. It floated a little while, and thinned away into nothing.

David Sessions / 23% of original / Volume 2, Number 1

Edward Smith

ENLARGEMENT

Volume 2, Number 1

i was standing at the altar
& jesus was there in a suit.
we stood around the front of the church
anxiety, emotions of struggle, held us.
then the man began
to go among us, putting his arms around us, speaking softly.
he was a perfectly ordinary man in a suit
but our christian hearts could tell who he was.
when my turn came he touched me, saying "ed, i can handle it."
of course i believed him
tho my mind could not picture
what it was he was talking about.

often i dream of san diego, home if i have one
swollen to huge proportions of nightmare
which i cling to precariously &
am not allowed to master.
                    last night
i returned to san diego high school
& it was during the summer
i was glad no one recognized me as i tampered
with the information in the glassed-in display showcases.
i hurried away before school opened for fall.

i remember mother & me
riding cablecars in san francisco
between halves of basic training
in some hopeless life when i became
a man with spit-shined shoes, a stronger
back, a marksman's badge, snug
green uniform, an acquaintance
with bus station sad
songs of 10,000 miles

at double-time springtime dust storm
green fatigues counting cadence marching
back along those roads, cold
with foggy sea breath & oily rifle steel
he searches
in the sand & brush, poison oak & manzanita,
tracing footprints of a curse, a look, emnity
no s.t.i. can see.

in san diego now
a mighty bridge spans the water where
near the very best fish markets the lowly
coronado ferry flanked by gulls used to unload.
the buonpensiero boys are grown.
if ever i have to really go back there
that someone knows me, knew me
when, surely he
can handle it
& the knots i have cruelly tied in hundreds of heartstrings
to make a seine for truth come unravelled
like shoelaces of children going to bed to dream of summer.
and what is next.   they think.
i have seen enough not to know
what is coming, except for, at the end of the chasm,
based upon the enlargement of what sensations–
exhaust smell of buses, political speeches, troop carriers,
novocaine, the smell of camelias, rooftop christmas
decorations–
have seemed, already unfamiliar–one is coming,
with dyed garments, alone, crimson, adamic
& i know him.

4 april–7 june 75

Charles Potts

I DREAM OF OAXACA

Volume 2, Number 1

for Clair Oursler

I dream of Oaxaca
and the lean and haggard vigil
born of love
                    I don't break laws
I reject civilizations

as I crawl out
onto the Frye Hotel
and run my tongue across
a taste of ugly roofs
winterproofed with tar
the blue winds of October blow
the particles of lite
into the whites
                    of my eyes
and sculpt
                of the total sound
a Puget flower
to watch the sea turn fuchsia
as the growth rings measure out
the water

o proton
            dendron
                        axiom
attic
        while the proteins
and the subteens
                        and assorted
deserters
of the void
                all listen to

the reassuring music

the Spaniel sings to me
blood welded
                    by a tire to the asphalt
'cept the flower of his head
bobbed in the air
                        in the 4 lanes
going by too fast
to stop
        on Nickerson

and his purebred open eyes adhere
to the pain
                in my frontal lobe
mounts a fear of tress pass
up the trapezoid
submerged in the terror
of my species

                tonite
there's no tomorrow
and its not too dark
the heli arc
                casts a pallor
on the particles of lite
picked from my eyes

remember how we spoke about
the great conspiracy
                        of turning
many into one
and spread out the fear
beyond
        rite now

the multiple facets

of the world turn on
to regenerate
the tissue of an artificial scar
grafted by the draft board
on my spirit

listen to the laser love
burn spots in
a part time Puget sun
I'll neither live nor die
for any madness other
than my own
as Mercury turns its cold side toward
the sun
          we dance around
in the miniscule rattle
of an all too Milky Way

and its not the splitting
that torments me
                    but

the coming
               back together

Freya Manfred

MY BASKETBALL BROTHER VERSUS WINDOM

Volume 2, Number 1

Nine players
shuttled down the floor,
red and white, blue and gold,
leaving the tenth,
my brother Fred, red and white,
politely grasping his stomach
above the groin
where Miller No. 31
had elbowed him in the balls.

My brother fell
on his back,
groaned and twitched
for five minutes.

My father
stood up straight nearly seven feet tall
and shouted,
"Number 31 is a killer, goddamit!"
My mother asked,
"What did Number 31 do that for?
D'you think he meant to hit Fred?"
I put one hand over my mouth
and chanted, "Oh Freddy, Oh Freddy,"
(as if he weren't 18 years old)
and groaned
because part of my body
that will never be part of my body
was hurt.

The referee
asked my brother not to swear,
AND he called the original foul

on my brother.

My father leaped seven feet
straight into the air
and said, "What?!?"
so loud
that six women sitting in front of us
exchanged wigs
and turned into hunchbacks.

We tried to jerk my father down
        out of the air
where he was floating
in a black cloud.
Everyone stared at mother and me
        as if we had
brought an Alaskan black bear
into the gym
without a chain.

My heart
kept leaving my chest
and going up for a rebound in my throat.
I called the referee OUT
on 40 technicals.
I pulled his black stripes
way out from his back
and let them snap back into the white stripes.

I did not enjoy the rest of the game.
Behind the prancing cheerleaders,
who pretended not to know about
their wide-split legs,
I saw monsters,
growing from human organs,
wounding and lashing
in the small town gym.

The sweetest thing of the night
was my own sweet brother
and his beautiful body
getting up off the floor
with all his blood inside.

David Koehne

LOUP-GAROU

Volume 2, Number 1

In France they burn His kind
Farmers bar their doors at night
Draw shutters tight against assaults
That never come, but firing at
Shadows anyway
When He passes cattle bellow
Sheep storm against their pens
Responding to a wildness that
Is not in Him
When the moon is full dreams
Break their women into half-moans
Wives and mothers contorting in bed
Aching for the harsh, savage breath
The hot teeth, the wildness that
Is not in Him
They say a silver bullet fired true
Into His heart can end these journeys
Can still the hound-bitch that howls
Whenever the stars form right
They say garlic and wolfbane strung
By an old woman and a young child
Can drive Him from their windows
They say running water, a mirror
A crucifix nailed to the door or a
Cross hung from the necks of their
Virgin daughters
Will offer protection
If a pentagram appears the child is
Bathed in vinegar-water and wrapped in
Pure-white sheets
If the fever takes hold a priest is
Called, and neighbors murmur prayers and
Old chants

In the fields, in the forests, on the
Dark country roads the Werewolf prowls
Dreaming of things He can not know of
Responding to a wildness that is not in Him

Tom Montag

from THE AFFLICTION OF GOODY CLASON

Volume 2, Number 1

4. The Testimony of Sarah Kecham

I was at Wescots house
Thomas Asten was there
Cateron Branch was in a fit

I asked "hows shee been
They said "shes had no fits
shes been a riding

I asked her "ride for me;
& soe she got to riding.
I asked her "Does the hors

have a name; she said "Jack;
I asked her "singe for me;
soe she sunge in Inglish

"Could you sing, I said,
in French; & soe she sung
in what they calld French

Thomas Astin said he knew
Cateron was bewitched
I sayd "I dont beleue that

I said "I doe not beleue
there are witches in town
He said "I know shes one

I haue hard it sayd
'if a persons bewitched
hould a sword ouer them

They will laugh themselves
to death; he took a sword
& held it ouer her

She laughed extremely.
I said sumthing to mean
"she knows about the sword

& soe she laughs; & Danil
made a sine to Austen
to hould the sword again

that she could not see it
& he did; she did not laugh
nor chang her countenance.

Richard Kostelanetz

Volume 2, Number 1

indistinct
face, with or
without glasses

easy smile

small droopy
breasts with
stretch marks

precociously
domesticated

enthusiastic
loquacious

powerful
hug
motorized
pelvis

loves to learn

scholarly ambitions

learns from lovers

authoritative speech

sister of
football
players

recently
divorced

stocky
though
not fat

emotional
reticence

fair
skin

5'4"
135 lbs
Dec 1947

maxi
skirts

long
well-
formed
inviting
face
dark-com
plexioned
smokes
5'4"
105 lbs
small
high
breasts
loyal
eager
helpful
suburban
"artistic"
culturally
ambitious
responsive
impatient
repressed
volunteer
preoccupied
affectionate
tight

spectacularly
very dark hair
warm-hearted
impressionable
shaven
crotch

This page is bypassed to allow for the two-page spread which follows.

Pat Dooley / 73% of original / Volume 1, Number 3

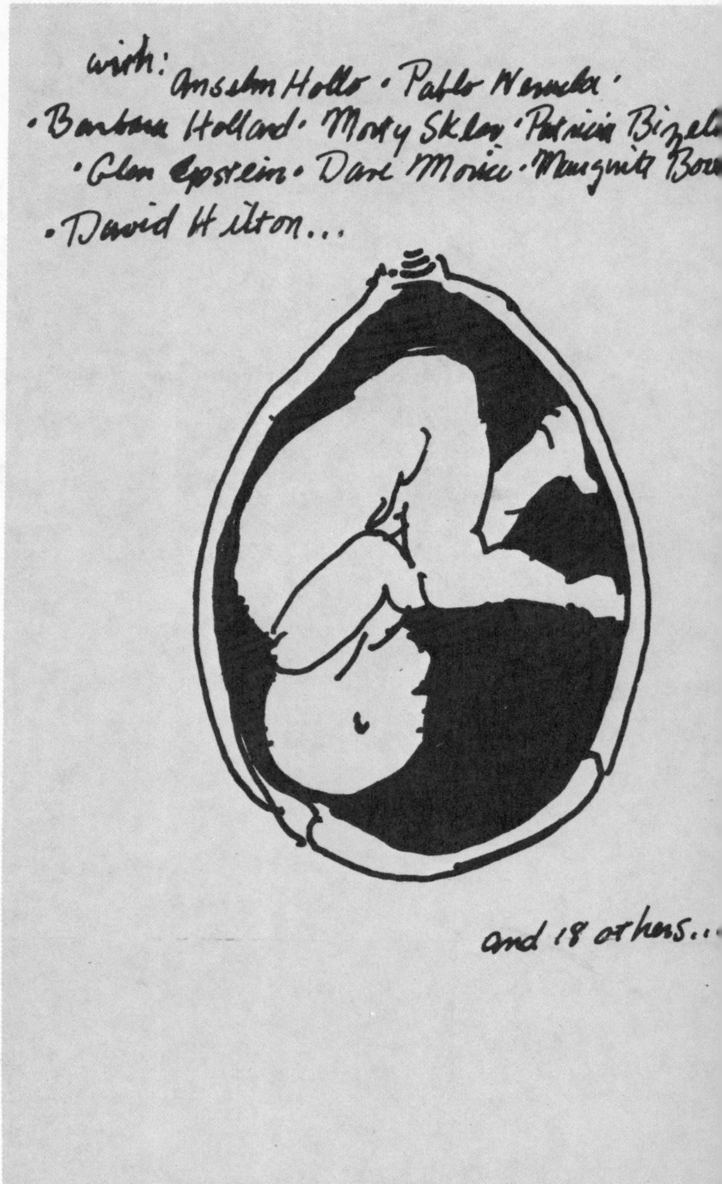

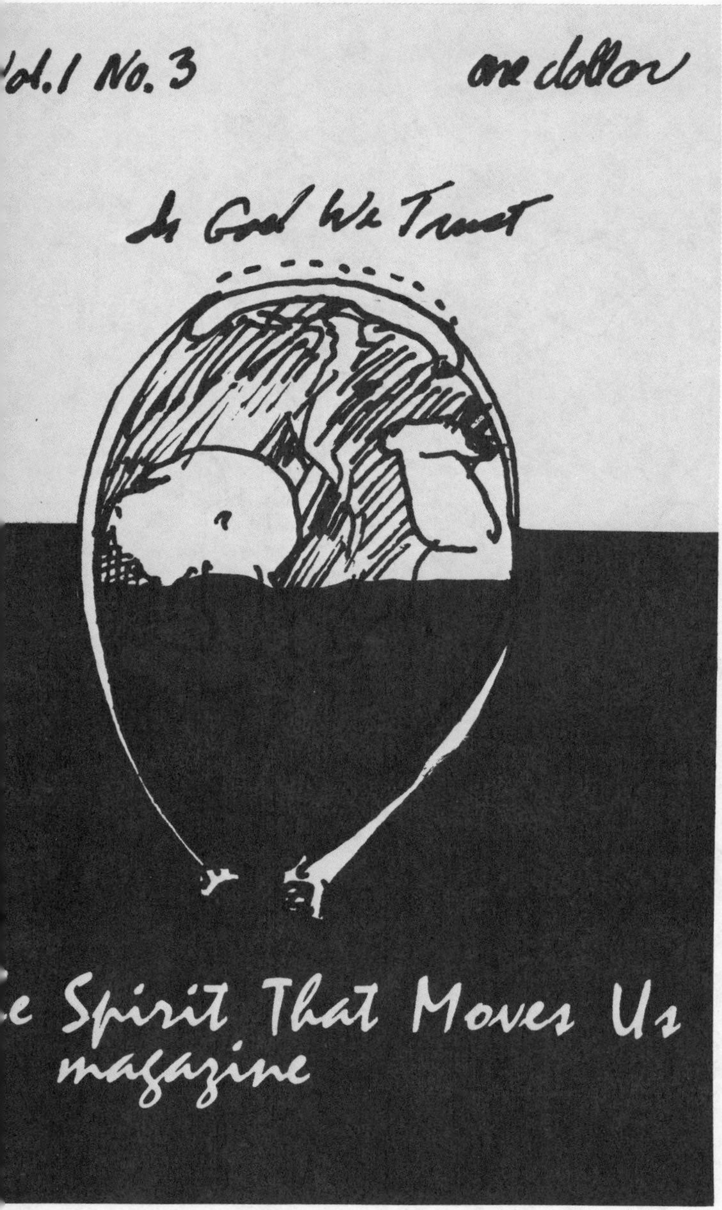
ol.1 No.3
one dollar
In God We Trust
e Spirit That Moves Us
magazine

Walt Phillips / 80% of original / Volume 1, Number 3

Lars Lundkvist

THREE POEMS

Volume 1, Number 3

Man across the moor. Looked for his calf,
came to a burning stone:

heaven's stone,
fallen in the ptarmigan's nest.

Lay down there. Night came on,
one star in the North.

Goatherds found his frosty bones,
dug a hole.

Saw spider. Heard curlew.
Ate trout for supper.

* * * * * * *

Lightning in the ground: the hazel-hen shrilled:
Take it!
Small man scampered off. Went
fast, over the mountain, into a valley.
There lay the lightning.
Lifted it onto his back, blew his nose
on the snow-crust. Turned around, blind.

Wailing in the Lapp tent. Dug in the backpack,
looked for his lightning. Found a branch,
a crooked one.

* * * * * * *

Once much ice was here. Then lived a man
who was a hunter and had three sons.

When the man died, each son wanted to grieve
the most, to get the man's spear.

The eldest took off his clothes, ran out
into the winter night.

"It is cold, father!" he yelled, froze to death.

The second son heated a stone red,
swallowed it.

"It is hot, father!" he yelled, burned up.

The third son said nothing. Tears fell
from his eyes onto the place where the spear lay.

Grass came up. Now the mountains are green.

—translated from the Swedish by
Gunnar Harding & Anselm Hollo

Morty Sklar / Volume 1, Number 2

Patricia Farewell

ON BECOMING AN EX-ALCOHOLIC

Volume 1, Number 2

a cup of coffee
shakes in your hand
around midnight
when you enter the woods
hoping to hear an owl.

sometimes the moonlight
guides you right through
to a perfect lookout,
a hollow or a hill
where you piece things together.

you never know
which tree he will sit in
what hour you can say
there is nothing in this world
like the sound of an owl.

David Sessions / 89% of original / Volume 1, Number 2

Sylvia Schuster / 53% of original / Volume 4, Number 1

Marty Ross

BO DIDDLEY AT FORTY-SEVEN

Volume 4, Number 1

You can see them all over town,
The Alan Freed castoffs,
The Dick Clark runaways,
The same lovable losers
That plucked their hearts in the grave
With James Dean,
And gave up the whole damn
Human race for dead.
Sometimes you see them
Under billiard signs in lower Manhattan,
Blowing kisses at the fags,
Staring down cops,
Or giving juicy lessons in vocabulary
To the secretaries on their yogurt breaks.
Mostly, though,
You find their leathery shadows
Skittering through bare bulb hallways,
Switchblades digging out
Forgotten names
On the stucco walls,
Whistling Del-Viking tunes
Under stairwells
Brittle with the impact
Of numberless feet,
And grinding out sweaty dances
In shuttered hop joints
With pale blondes
In Clinton sweaters
And puffy ankle socks.
Down streets that fit like a bad suit
Walk the wingless teen angels,
Searching for a jukebox
That looks like a Buck Rogers console,

Scott Simmer

FOURTH OF JULY ADDRESS. DESERTED RAILROAD TUNNEL, COLORADO. CONTINENTAL DIVIDE.

Volume 4, Number 1

You're climbing toward 12,000 feet
and will soon be intoxicated on thin air.
Your voice returns from the valley
numbed by glaciers and rockslides.

Something skitters along the ridge.
These are marmots. They have celebrated
for sixty years the tearing up of the rails
by eating all wood not dipped in creosote.

Fifty-thousand men dug this ore road
to link mines at T'helluride and Ouray
with Denver. This was their moonshot,
their place to chip away at the impossible.

"Build the highest tunnel on the planet"
the want ads read. Wages were good—
graveyard paid eighteen dollars a day,
but most men lasted only a week.

Read the gnawed sign at the tunnel mouth:
"Each shift walked to their shacks
roped together, their collective heat
protecting them from the cold."

Say the word "avalanche"
so that it glissades off your tongue
and know how twelve-hundred men
died on the palisade.

A mile down an eddy of snow

uncovered one frozen, crazed face
when the first freight
labored up the western grade.

From the pass over the tunnel
you can see the moraine
reclaiming the land.
Rocks halve the engine turnaround.

The basement of the saloon, where whores
kissed away the ring of dynamite blasts,
is being filled by a cirque
gouged out of a mountain.

You wonder what brought you here
to this cusp, this muscular sidetrack
of history, near the headwaters
of the Arkansas and Colorado Rivers.

You're three-thousand feet above treeline
and think you see a roman candle
spitting on the horizon where a scrub pine
is whipping in and out of the sun.

Willing to give up an entire
Johnny Maestro collection
For a quiet place
Out of the jetstream,
A place where a funky dude
Can sip Knickerbockers in the dark
And try and figure out
How the hell
Bo Diddley can be
Forty-seven.

Alberto Rios

MORNING

Volume 4, Number 1

Everyday I saw a man
who wore a suit
and had a beard hid under his skin.
It was black.
I could see it in the light
see its darkness
and it came out through his eyes
precisely in their centers
when he looked at me.
Under his suit, under his shirt,
undershirt, it started coming
through his chest and from his back.
He thought about his beard
because it was tangled in his head.
It made him unhappy
and his head was heavy
and sometimes he rested it in his hands
and let his beard come through
them, the backs of his
palms and fingers.
He cradled his head in those hands
which might have kept it,
which might have grown into his head
but I would come in, and call him, *daddy*,
and they would let go.

Ronald Koertge

DEMANDS OF THE MOLARS

Volume 4, Number 1

Next door, the neighbors are breeding
their purebreds:
"Alright, now, do your stuff."
"Listen to Daddy, Pollen Ears."
"Get hot, bitch. C'mon."
"Try for Momma, Adios Feet."
"Quit kidding around. We've got pups
promised yesterday."

The beasts turn. They leap on
their owners. They rend and tear
until nothing remains.

I see a chance to finance 1000 meals
and hustle over, recorder on microphone!
"To begin, why did you always shit
on my lawn?"
"Up until now," they reply in unison,
"it was what we did best."

Jim Mulac / 73% of original / Volume 5, Numbers 1 & 2

William Kloefkorn

OUT-AND-DOWN PATTERN

Volume 5, Numbers 1 & 2

My young son pushes a football into my stomach
and tells me that he is going to run
an out-and-down pattern,
and before I can check the signals
already he is half way across the front lawn,
approaching the year-old mountain ash,
and I turn the football slowly in my hands,
my fingers like tentacles
exploring the seams,
searching the lacing,
and by the time I have the ball positioned
just so against the grain-tight leather,
he has made his cut downfield
and is now well beyond the mountain ash,
approaching the linden,
and I pump my arm once, then once again,
and let fire.

The ball in a high arc
rises up and out and over the linden,
up and out over the figure
that has now crossed the street,
that is now all the way to Leighton Avenue,
now far beyond,
the arms outstretched,
the head as I remember it
turned back, as I remember it
the small voice calling.

And the ball at the height of its high arc
begins now to drift,
to float as if weightless
atop the streetlights and the trees,

becoming at last that first bright star in the west.

Late into an early morning
I stand on the front porch,
looking into my hands.

My son is gone.

The berries on the mountain ash
are bursting red this year,
and on the linden
blossoms spread like children.

Paul Stutts / 47% of original / Volume 5, Numbers 1 & 2

Meto Jovanovski

THE MAN IN THE BLUE SUIT

Volume 5, Numbers 1 & 2

EVERYONE noticed his bright blue suit. He walked upright with steady steps and looked straight ahead and far in front of himself. The rhythms of the lines in the pavement passed beneath his feet, unrecorded.

When he came to the newspaper kiosk, he stopped, but he did not turn. Rigid as a mannequin, he put a hand into a pocket, withdrew a coin, and, after placing it on the counter, turned his head just a bit, only to see which paper he would take. Then he stretched his hand out, folded the newspaper which was given him, and with one motion placed it under his arm and began walking as before, coldly upright, looking far ahead of his steps.

There was a bus stop on the corner, and when he approached it, he raised his eyes in the direction of the board on the post beside it. It was the action of a sensible man.

At the top of the board, above the smaller print, the number thirteen was written. The man in the blue suit stopped beneath it. He moved one leg slightly outward, took his newspaper in his hand, opened it, and began reading.

Meanwhile, the people passing up and down along the street were engaged in the living of their own lives. Some of them cast an eye at the man in the blue suit, who continued standing just beneath the board which marked the bus stop.

From the dark entrance of the hospital came two peasants, each with a sack on his back. They walked, silent and bent, looking at the pavement, to the bus stop, where they stopped, at the edge of the pavement and a little beyond the man in the blue suit. There they stood, but there was wonder in their eyes, for they did not know at all whether it was all right to wait or not.

The man in the blue suit glanced at them, discreetly but questioningly. Then, without hiding his intolerance, he continued his reading. The peasants continued to stand in their places, now almost dozing in the sun, their heads hanging loosely from their thin, hair-covered necks. But they stood together, beside each other and at a little distance from the man in the blue suit.

The man in the blue suit cast another glance in the direction of the peasants, and this one was less discreet, almost disapproving. Now even a flash of anger could be seen in his eyes. Keeping his newspaper in his right hand, he stretched out his left toward the peasant nearer him. Rather squeamishly he touched the peasant on the shoulder. When the peasant, aroused and confused, turned questioningly toward him, the man in the blue suit said, "Are you waiting for a bus?"

"Yes," said the peasant.

Now the other peasant began to be aware that something was taking place.

"Then," said the man in the blue suit, "You should queue up in the line."

They looked at him in wonder and then slightly downward. They did not want to accept what he had said. There was no line for them. But they yielded. They just moved slightly.

"When people are waiting for a bus they stand one behind the other and not beside one another," said the man in the blue suit. The two peasants looked at one another and moved to form a proper queue, one behind the other behind the man in the blue suit.

Then the man in the blue suit turned a page of his newspaper and went on with his reading.

The two men behind him stood unmovingly but anxious in their impotence. It seemed that they would give anything only to be able to turn to one another, to look trustingly at one another; that would explain everything. But they did not dare. They must be content to look upon the back of the man in the blue suit.

That man looked at his watch for a moment and then returned to his reading. But when a middle-aged man came to the bus stop, the man in the blue suit took notice of him.

He noticed how impatiently the newcomer walked up and

down behind the three of them, how he glanced up the street then out in front of himself then thrust his hands in his pockets, and how confused he seemed in his impatience and boredom. Then the newcomer turned toward the three in the queue and began to look them over. He moved his eyes from one to the other, as if they were notes on a musical scale, until he met the eyes of the man in the blue suit. Then he turned again towards the street and, bending a little, thrust his hands into his pockets again and, bringing his two feet exactly together, began to observe the toes of his shoes. The two peasants, expectantly and protestingly, looked at the man and then at the man in the blue suit.

"Fellow," they heard the voice of the man in the blue suit, and felt relieved and lively. The newcomer turned curiously around, not sure to whom the word was addressed. "I think," said the man in the blue suit, looking at him, "that you should stand in line."

The newcomer opened his mouth and looked at a point in space in front of the speaker. He was preparing his resistance. But when he met the look of the man in the blue suit, he said nothing but swallowed imperceptably and moved unwillingly to take his place in the line.

The man in the blue suit went on reading; he did not seem to be at all impatient.

After that a young man and a girl came. They were very interested in one another, so much so that they did not even notice the queue. They stopped somewhere near the two peasants, the young man listening with attention to the young girl's chattering.

The man in the blue suit paid them no attention.

The man who now stood last in the queue looked around the peasants toward the man in the blue suit, expecting to see him turning. Then the man in the blue suit appeared to notice the couple; he looked at the man at the end as if to tell him that he should take the matter in his own hands. But the man at the end seemed nervous, so the man in the blue suit looked away to the couple and said, "We hope you will observe the queue."

The young man and the girl glanced at the queue and confronted four pairs of eyes and four silent rebukes. They were a bit disturbed for they wished to be liked. Because of this wish, they moved to the end of the line, but there they stood beside one another. And they would have remained thus, had the man in front of them not continued to look at them.

The man in the blue suit turned another page of his newspaper and moved his eyes up and down its columns.

After that others who came to the bus stop and, out of habit, took random places alongside of the others, met the eyes of the men in front of the line and, finding the imperative of those eyes irresistable, finally took their places in line. Thus, a long line was formed.

But the bus did not come. The man in the blue suit again looked at his watch and then refolded his newspaper. Then he folded the paper again and put it in his pocket. Then he stood still, facing the street, and waited for the bus.

According to the watch of the man in the blue suit, it should have arrived; but the bus did not appear. Then the man turned toward the line. The two peasants were beside him. He said, in a low voice, distinctly but to no one in particular, "If there were order wherever it is necessary this would not happen."

Only the nearer peasant heard the words, but he turned to his companion and gave him a questioning look. The companion did not even understand that there was something which needed to be understood. He was ready to spit, yet somehow the blue sky at which he was staring prevented him from doing so.

Across the street from the bus stop a young man, with a large black moustache and a necktie upon which was painted a palm tree and a naked woman, stopped and noticed the line of people, so neatly queued up to offer themselves as customers for the city's public transit system. The man in the blue suit noticed his mocking look. Then finally bus number thirteen could be seen approaching.

The people in the line turned to watch it and seemed to be on the verge of moving from their places. The man in the blue suit sensed that the line might shorten or even break now, so he cast his eyes along its length. He tried to meet each pair of eyes along the row. And the queue calmed.

The bus made its stop so that its entrance door opened just in front of the man in the blue suit. He was just about to step up when the young man from across the street appeared from around the rear of the bus, his mouth pursed, whistling. With eyes full of irony he stepped up, ahead of the man in the blue suit. For a moment it seemed that the young man would enter the bus first, but the man in the blue suit put his right arm up and his hand on the side of the rear door and thus blocked the young man's way.

Then the man in the blue suit turned his head toward the peasant beside him and said, "You, please step up." The peasant, amazed, hesitated, not knowing whether it was right to enter the bus or not. "Please, please," the man in the blue suit said to him.

So the peasant stepped up. Immediately, the other peasant followed. The young man from the other side of the street stopped whistling and stared at this keeper of public order. He wanted to push his shoulder against the chest of the man in the blue suit, to force him backwards into the line of entering passengers. But he could not, there was a terrible warning in the man's eyes.

So the young man had to wait. It was very difficult for him to meet the eyes of those in the line, all of whom were looking at him with undisguised contempt. So he looked away, toward the entrance of the hospital. He noticed two attendants coming toward him from its back door.

The people in the line slowly entered the bus. The last was a bent old man, whom the man in the blue suit assisted in his long step up. Then the man in the blue suit sent a final look, full of rebuke, at the young man, turned, and waited to step up into the bus behind the bent old man.

The young man noticed that the attendants were running

and were much nearer than he expected. In fact, now they were just behind the man in the blue suit. One of his feet was already on the step when he noticed them also. "Do you want me?" said the man in the blue suit.

Reaching for his arm which already grasped the vertical bar on the bus entrance, one attendant nodded his head.

"Yes. . . ."

"It was good of you to be on time," said the man in the blue suit. He removed his foot from the step.

The young man looked mockingly at him as they turned him away, then he stepped up and into the bus.

"What a strange thing," said one of the passengers who had stood in the row.

"He seemed so wise," said another.

Then several of those who had been waiting in the line looked out the window toward the hospital. There, entering at the dark door, were the two attendants, on either side of the man in the blue suit.

There was a silence among many on the bus. The conductor had not noticed anything, and when the last passenger had entered, he gave the signal for the driver to start up.

-translated from the Macedonian by the author with Milne Holton

Mike Blackmore / 30% of original / Volume 5, Numbers 1 & 2

Judy Ray / *The Farm In Calabria* (pblshd. back-to-back w/Vol. 5, Nos. 1 & 2)

David Ray

MULBERRIES

The Farm In Calabria (part of Vol. 5, Nos. 1 & 2)

I brush into a pile
the fallen mulberries,
good for nothing but to make us
slip and break our bones,
and so I give them to my youngest
trees, to my linden and my birch,
to nourish them.
I never want my children
to eat mulberries,
because once upon a time
I had to live on them,
sitting with my sister
in the branches. We were
bitter, having nothing else,
nothing save hate,
which we work now
into proverbs, as I sweep
into a pile the fallout-
dusted berries
which are good for nothing
in modern times
though the Chinese found them
first-rate for paintings
on silk, and children once
took them into their bellies
with defeat.

Honore Daumier / Volume 5, Number 3

Garrett Kaoru Hongo

AND YOUR SOUL SHALL DANCE

Cross-Fertilization: The Human Spirit As Place

—for Wakako Yamauchi

Walking to school beside fields
of tomatoes and summer squash,
alone and humming a Japanese love song,
you've concealed a copy of *Photoplay*
between your algebra and English texts.
Your knee socks, saddle shoes, plaid dress,
and blouse, long-sleeved and white
with ruffles down the front,
come from a Sears catalogue
and neatly complement your new Toni curls.
All of this sets you apart from the landscape:
flat valley grooved with irrigation ditches,
a tractor grinding through alkaline earth,
the short stands of windbreak eucalyptus
shuttering the desert wind
from a small cluster of wooden shacks
where your mother hangs the wash.
You want to go somewhere.
Somewhere far away from all the dust
and sorting machines and acres of lettuce.
Someplace where you might be kissed
by someone with smooth, artistic hands.
When you turn into the schoolyard,
the flagpole gleams like a knifeblade in the sun,
and classmates scatter like chickens,
shooed by the storm brooding on your horizon.

23:X:75

Lennart Bruce

THE ROAD MOVES UP TO ME

Cross-Fertilization: The Human Spirit As Place

nervously entering
the focus of my being,
a hole opens:

a subway
through the city
of brain's precious jelly

a play between loose connections
crossed by a flame
running through me, it lifts me

through rapids of blood
roars me through the noise of hearing
flashes me through touch and vision.

Sunlight from an unknown explosion
holds me in cupped hands
of energy

The road leads
to the forgotten, I follow
its steep, narrow stairs

They lead back to the sky
leaves whirling in its chimney

Around the outlines of my shoulders
and on top of them there's still another
head composed of nothing but light

When I was a baby (between wars)
mother took me to the doctor because

I had too small a head

The doctor laughed at her

In there I hear voices.
Brain waves stretch
Fitted onto them is the skin

which wrinkles the forehead
and smooths it with the smile
and deepest in there

the domesticated madness
bends and turns hidden behind
its own outstretched hand.

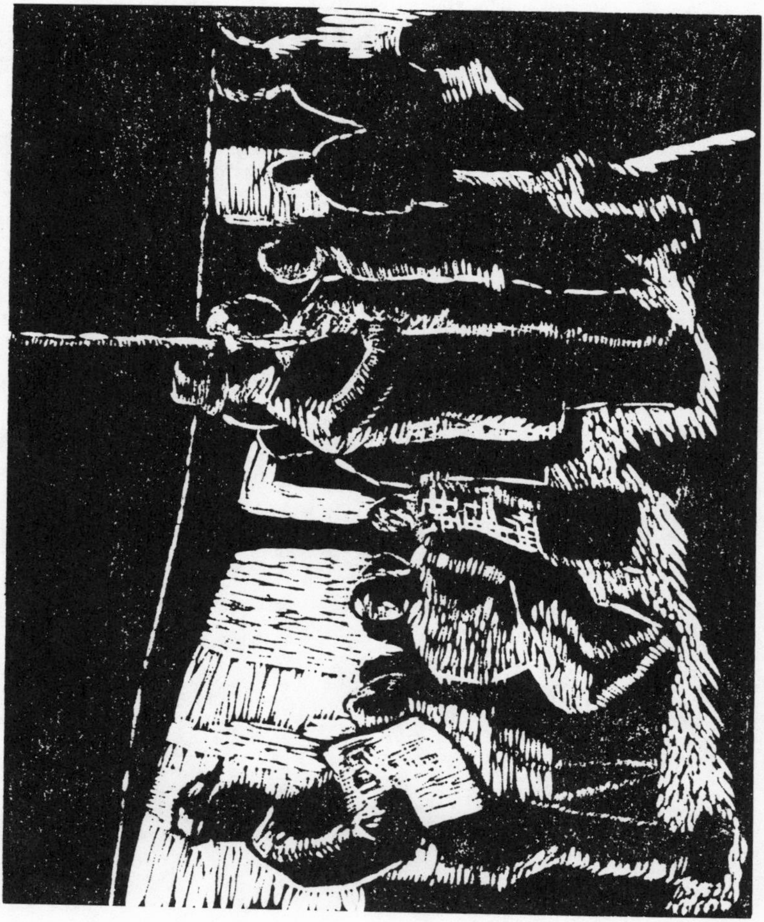

A. McA. Miller

MISS PAAM

Cross-Fertilization: The Human Spirit As Place

Ben Cat, Vietnam

Rain circled on your hooch. Late every night
Your legs, like new *Go Mat*, forked yellow brown.
If I plant you in the mud will you grow up?

Southeast winds had slithered off of Nam:
By chopper, R & R was one long hop.
If you try to dam the Mekong, then you drown.

Rice ponds were pooling over. On my lap
You rode like *Nipa* bobbing, tight as *Tram*
If I plant you in the mud will you grow up?

In Georgia I'm a distant, different man.
My woman is a long-nose, white and slack.
If you try to dam the Mekong, then you drown.

You were slippery in the eye, but from the hip
You paced as straight as rain walks through the *Quan*;
If I plant you in the mud will you grow up?

Outside the hooch, rain fell forever down.
We paddled in our bodies like the rain.
If I plant you in the mud, will you grow up?
If you try to dam the Mekong, then you drown.

Hooch, hut; *Go Mat*, yellowish brown ripsawed for construction work; *chopper*, helicopter; *R & R*, military leave for Rest & Recuperation; *Nipa*, mangrove with slender floating seeds; *Tram*, a dense wood, often flawed in the grain; *Quan*, a province or small state.

Haywood Jackson

OUT OF THE DEEPNESS

Cross-Fertilization: The Human Spirit As Place

High in the mountains of Soviet Armenia
at Lake Sevan: the sun, clean, bright,
warming the cool thin air off the reaches
of the lake, the skin of our arms and faces.
Dark, hopeful eyes of children wanting gum,
candy, something American. They bring
bouquets of wild red flowers.
The bus driver, after the long engineheating
climb out of Yerevan, opens the gray hood,
shows me the leak in the radiator, shrugs,
and adds more water. I buy a bottle
of one ruble wine at the "gastronom" here
(for later, for the remainder of the run
over the cloudhung mountains to Georgia).

We stop for lunch, for trout freshly brought
out of the deepness of the lake.

A busload of Instanbul Armenians
fill up a long table beside us.
They have yet to know their first, cherished
glimpse of Ararat. Now they rise, singing
the saddest sounding song I've ever heard.
Their wineglasses catch the light of the sun.
The eaglefaced grandfather, surprising
with a voice of warm mercury, vibrant cadences
leads them in a toast:
"To the Americans! To Peace!"
My skin buzzes. I turn,
and touch my glass to his.

Wolfgang Kohlhaase

INVENTION OF A LANGUAGE

Cross-Fertilization: The Human Spirit As Place

TEN numbers are called out over the loudspeaker, the tenth is his. Straat feels neither fear nor hope. He steps out of the line, reels to and fro past backs and faces to the end of his block, turns right and makes his way painstakingly towards the man who called him up, the man standing on a platform, a desk with papers and a microphone in front of him.

It is April in the year forty-four. Straat, tenth in the row which has lined up face to the wall, is deadly tired although it is early in the day, and he is so young. The sky which he can see when he looks up and over the roof of the guardhouse is grey and rainy. Just a little way off under the clouds, just a little way across the world, lies Holland. From there Straat and five others had been brought here, a hundred days ago, a long, long time ago. Why? So that he might sweat and freeze, so that he might carry stones, be beaten, lie in filth, sleep on planks, eat putrid vegetables and finally cease to exist. But before that happens, still breathing, still able to look about, he is to forget who he was. And he has almost forgotten. Unimaginable that the place where he was born over there not far off at the end of the sky still exists, that earth and water, his parents, the evenings, the smell which was different in the girls' class, the implements behind the glass door of the cupboard, physics, still exist. Six semesters of that–unimaginable. Because the law of the conservation of energy is no longer valid. No longer valid for those who run up and down the big stairway carrying stones, running the gauntlet between clubs and gun sights, from one darkness to the other. Six students of physics, five are lost and gone. The sixth, deadly tired, is Straat, and today he is not going to the quarry because his number has been called up.

Ten men, but where are they going? To the bunker? To the medical quarters? A capo wearing a white jacket, conducts them to the kitchen. A stone building, tiled inside. Six brightly polished kettles in which the stinking soup is cooked. But they weren't called because of the soup. They were called because of the potatoes.

The commandant is giving a party for his cronies. On such occasions, the guards, the killers, the paymaster, the wardens, the administrators, the torturers, the clerks, the doctor sit together at long tables; it's all very *gemutlich*. The evening rests on three pillars: first of all cameraderie, secondly beer, thirdly roast pork and potato salad. That's why ten stools are now standing in the kitchen, ten baskets with potatoes next to them, ten basins for the refuse in front of them, a metal tub in the middle and Straat, sitting on one of the stools.

It is warm and quiet in the kitchen. The nearby quarry is far away. An SS-man is sitting in a cubicle next to the door, reading. Only the capo comes in now and then to stand by the potato-peelers and watch them work. Not out of meanness, just professional interest. All the same, Straat's hands begin to tremble, he is not a practised peeler, his peel is too thick, he is too slow under the shadow of the capo who stares at his hands. The capo leaves only to come back again. Straat works faster but it's no use, the inevitable question has already been formed:

"What did you do before, eh?"

"Student," says Straat without looking up, continuing to peel with fluttering hands. Any minute now he'll be kicked. The SS-man behind the window will look up from his book. And then? But the capo only says:

"All over with the studying now, eh?"

At noon they get a bowl of steaming soup, from the top, in which a few strands of meat are swimming about. And a second bowl, filled to the brim. Straat, leaning against the wall of the kitchen building with all that soup inside the skeleton which is his body, is quite still. Suddenly he's not hungry any more. No quarry. No shouting. Far away, under the electric fence where no one is allowed to go, he discovers a shimmer of green and remembers it's April. The capo, watching him, strolls up and asks:

"What did you study, man?"

"Physics."

"I see," says the capo, as if completely in the know.

In the afternoon Straat is less afraid when the capo saunters up to plant himself beside him. A ray of sunshine creeps into the kitchen, the potatoes thud into the water, the regular squad, in white aprons, is cutting bread for the next day; who would think that at this very minute someone, here and there, not far away, is dying in the sand. The capo, standing next to Straat, suddenly feels the need to unburden himself.

"Damn it all," he says, "when I get out of here, after the war, I'm going to Persia."

It seems that the capo has a brother in Persia, so he tells Straat, who just made it in time, in thirty-nine, and is now sitting pretty, a big businessman, and the capo's sitting here like the idiot he is.

"You're Dutch," says the capo. "What do you think, is Persia a good place to go?"

"I'm sure it is," says Straat. He peels and peels, only he doesn't peel quite as fast as before. The capo, in the soft afternoon light, nods his head like someone who feels he's understood, and sighs:

"Pity about all that lost time, all that beautiful time. If at least one could learn Persian here."

He looks troubled, his face, lined with worry, is like the face of an honest friend, a man almost forty, well-fed compared with the ruins sitting there in a circle; fate threw him down and lifted him up again, but he's been suckered all the same. That's the way it goes, man. And suddenly Straat hears himself say:

"I know Persian."

The capo throws him a long look out of his watery eyes unbelieving at first, then doubting, then almost tender.

"You know Persian?"

Straat nods, his face rigid.

"Come with me."

The capo runs off, Straat follows him, stumbling into the office cubicle.

"Now then, tell me, how come you know Persian?"

There's no going back for Straat any more. One doesn't joke with a capo, least of all if it takes just one blow to make you fall never to get up again. Not that Straat wants to joke, all he wants is not to go back to the quarry where he would perish; he wants to stay in the kitchen where he can sit on a stool like a human being and peel potatoes, where he will get a bowl of soup. The only thing he fears is that his voice will fail him, but it doesn't, it's just very feeble. He says:

"I was in Persia, before the war."

"Man almighty, d'you know what will happen to you if you don't tell the truth?"

Straat's eyes reflect such terror, that the capo is certain he knows what would be in store for him.

"All right then, how d'you say good morning?"

"*Dalam*," says Straat.

"And shit?"

Straat takes too long, the capo becomes impatient.

"There must be a word for shit."

"*Tupa*," says Straat.

"*Tupa*," the capo repeats, deeply moved. Then he says: "You're peeling for your life now."

So much for what they said. But the consequences are tremendous. For example, kitchen capo Battenbach intercepts *Rottenfuhrer* Roeder when the latter reappears after a lengthy meal. He explains to Roeder that he's been needing another man in the squad for a long time, he had never found the right one but now he'd noticed someone because of his special aptitude. All the while the *Rottenfuhrer* nods his head. He wouldn't mind taking a look at such an outstanding man. With Battenbach in his wake, he stalks over to the potato-peelers and stares at the half-starved Dutchman, formerly student of physics, six semesters, but that is of no interest to Roeder. What interests him is what he can see, and he sees that this man has no idea at all of the art of potato-peeling, however desperately he may be trying. But that doesn't matter, because twice a week the *Rottenfuhrer* takes home a piece of sausage, Sundays a roast and now and then a square of margarine. All that with Battenbach's help. So Roeder nods a second time, goes back to his cubicle, writes name and number on a piece of paper. Later in the day, this piece of paper reaches labour statistics and from there it goes to the labour squad leader. At roll call the next morning, which dawns bright and humid, Straat is the only one of the ten potato-peelers to return to the kitchen, where Battenbach gives him a friendly slap on the back.

Now Straat is Battenbach's man. He will not be burnt to cinders, he will get bread and soup to put him back on his feet again. It would be a pity with a brain like that, Battenbach thinks to himself and rubs his hands, though they may have locked him up for procuring, unpolitical, they can't prevent him from learning Persian now. Even Roeder who hangs around Straat during those first days, trying to understand what's going on does not know, he cannot possibly know, that the bond between the well-fed capo and the hungry Dutchman is a very particular language. But even Battenbach cannot know that this language doesn't even exist. Only Straat knows. He alone determines rules and words. How many words will he need, on how many days?

At noon, as soon as *Rottenfuhrer* Roeder has gone to eat Battenbach calls Straat to the orderly-room, sits down at the table, calm and concentrated, crumpled paper and pencil stub in front of him, prepared to acquire a knowledge of Persian. On the first day he wants to hear something about Persia in general. Straat lets the climate be hot, the women beautiful, the poor poor and the rich rich. Battenbach is satisfied, that's how he had imagined it. Personally he used to be in the entertainment business, do they have that there too? Brothels? Straat doesn't understand quickly enough; Battenbach explains. Yes, of course, absolutely, says Straat. And Battenbach nods his head, he'd thought as much. But now he wants to learn a few words: schnaps, police, thank you, please, table, chair, canteen, steak. Straat can't afford to hesitate, not on the first day. He translates every word, one after the other: *alan, monato, laps, nam, toki, sol, oltok, runidam, steak.* That's a borrowed word, Straat says, it's international. Painstakingly,

Battenbach writes everything down.

In the evening, under the tattered blanket, the shoulder of his neighbour, the one who shares his bunk, touching his own, laming weariness weighing on his eyes—in the evening Straat searches for words and above all for a system with which to remember them. He is wrapped up in the heavy breathing of the exhausted; the man next to him groans in his sleep; Straat's lips form words which no one has ever heard before: *or, tal, mel, meb,* which means: I, you, he, she, it.

Battenbach's fist strikes him between the eyes, Battenbach kicks his shinbone, beats him against the wall; Battenbach is trembling with rage and disappointment. Because of *runidam*, the Persian word for canteen. Straat had invented it that very first day and now that Battenbach asked him again he's forgotten it. Straat knew that it had slipped his mind, but Battenbach hadn't allowed him to throw even one glance at his papers; he had waited two days, had noted new words, had Straat spell them out for him in order to prevent Straat from looking over his shoulder, and now he has him between his fists, and he's going to expose this Dutch swine before the midday break is over. It's been ten years since he was in Persia, screams Straat desperately, he was still a child then and *runidam* is a very rare word, it was just by chance that he had remembered it, actually canteen was *mardam*, but if he didn't get pencil and paper soon he will never be able to refresh his memory after such a long time.

"I'll let you rot in hell," says Battenbach. Then there is silence. Straat is leaning against the wall, looking at the capo with frightened eyes, and Battenbach looks at the boy's forehead where the skin is tight and grey, sees the vein beating at his temple, damn it all, if only he could look inside his head. Slowly doubt begins to mingle with suspicion, doubt which he would like to give in to. For in those few days already the language has taken hold of him; during the empty evenings when he stands at his window looking across the drill ground, filled with a dull hatred against the world, haunted by memories of women, he has with the help of those Persian words which are so difficult to learn, suddenly become a man who makes good use of every hour, who thinks ahead, who has his secret, his far-reaching plans.

"If you're cheating me my lad, if you don't know Persian," says Battenbach, and the monstrosity of this thought makes his voice tremble. "I do," Straat says, "I do know Persian. Only it was such a long time ago." From now on Straat is in possession of paper and pencil, riches for which one can be thrown into the bunker. If they catch him Battenbach won't know a thing about it. Straat hides the pencil in his shoe and the paper in his cap. Above the brain, between his shorn head and the material of the cap, he carries the language. At roll call he has to be careful, especially at the command "caps off." The language might fall out. It could be discovered, taken from him. Then, whatever happens, he is lost; his guards or his pupil will beat him to death. Every evening he also hides a piece of bread or a few potatoes under his clothes, for his bunk-sharing comrade, an electrician from Groningen, quarry squad, who only weighs ninety pounds.

At night Straat works on his language. He twists letters and syllables about, invents words. The special German institutions which surround him are integrated in his language. He gives them a sound which carries him away, not to Persia but to some strange, quiet world and at such moments he escapes from their horrible meaning. *Rium, rema, matori, muro, cemato, icre, tame, muir, rotam, cretum, orite, mecor, cumo, emati, catu, meri, tamcu, taritora.*

All that he makes out of crematorium. He does the same with arrest and barracks, with quarry and barbed wire and even with Battenbach, his protector, who in this way learns out of his very self. The greasy, black smoke becomes *sokem*, the wind.

In the dark, Straat writes the words on a piece of paper, as small as possible. He hides the paper in his cap and puts the cap under the straw mattress. He does not invent more than five words a night, thirty a week, that's enough even for Battenbach. They leave out Sundays. Straat eats two bowls of soup every day, he gets stronger, he notices that it's summer, the faint scent of lupins in full bloom comes from the distant fields. One day a Dutchman from labour statistics is waiting for him in the latrine.

"What goes on between you and the capo in his room every day?"

"What is that to you," says Straat suspiciously.

The Dutchman looks at him with indulgence. He says: "You didn't get to peel potatoes by chance, you know. We put your name on the list, because you were the last of the students. So that you'd have one day to recuperate. Then Battenbach asked for you. Why?"

It was quiet but for the humming of the green, glittering flies. And in the eyes of the other man Straat sees not only suspicion, but fear and sympathy and also relentlessness and severity; at that moment he feels that this language, which only he knows, can protect him but also destroy him, because it puts him above his fellow prisoners. But he is afraid to divulge his secret, even to someone who could be his friend, for who is really a friend? More than anyone else perhaps the boy from Groningen, next to him on the bunk, whom he gives bread, potatoes and new courage, but he does not reveal his secret even to him.

Summer forty-four.

A silver braid of bombers draws across German skies. Straat makes a word for life, he calls it *sawal*. And a word for apple tree, it's called *pollimolli*. Just for fun, not to please Battenbach. At his own request, Battenbach learns numbers and idioms and expressions from the entertainment business. When Battenbach is in a bad mood Straat invents words of revenge. One of them is: *suliduladornatlam*. Battenbach tries to refuse, he is furious, says he needs practical Persian for everyday use. But Straat explains that this is the greeting usual in the country, impossible to cross a threshold in Persia without *suliduladornatlam*.

"*Tupa*," says Battenbach like an old Persian. And while Straat's physics-trained mind, now no longer paralysed by hunger, no longer stupefied by fear, is thinking out the framework for a new language, some fifty men around him are dying, day after day, week after week, their flesh is burnt, their brain fizzles out, their souls fly up to the heaven of their belief; maybe their mouths have formed a last word before they leave, a word which makes its long way from one person to the other, across countries, finally, perhaps, to reach those who are waiting for it.

Straat's language will reach no one but Battenbach, it will not carry a message, it represents nothing but itself, it saves the life of the man who thought it up, and makes another man who is laboriously learning it—a dirty dog not a bloodhound—just a little more gentle. Otherwise it is quite useless. But Straat needs the imagination of great discoveries, the courage of great hypotheses, the effort of great experiments for his language. And Battenbach, kitchen capo, procurer from Hamburg, needs the diligent stupidity which took him through school.

One August morning, his face patchy, his tongue protruding from his mouth, he is carried from the drill ground, where he had collapsed, to the medial room. For three days, lying on a straw mattress on the floor, he is delirious, the orderlies hear him talk in confused Dutch, but he also mumbles unintelligible prattle, a string of words which don't make sense. One day it looks as though he'll make it, he is stronger than the others, but is he still in his right mind? The orderly will pass along the rows with his syringe. He heals all pain with a shot of air, a dead man is no longer sick. When he hears Straat screaming he will declare him insane, will note down his number, push back his sleeve and search for the vein. The orderly pulls Straat by the feet into an adjoining room where the dead are lying; no one will hear him here, no one will look for him here. Straat comes to. In the warm sunlight which shines through the window he looks at his fellow men, rigid, in the ridiculous distortions of the last moments, pupils fixed forever, mouths ripped wide open as if to scream. And he? Is he still alive? He has a voice with which he can howl like a wolf, with which he can pronounce words which make everyone wonder, except his silent companions. Is he one of them now?

Before the hearse, lined with sheet zinc, comes, Straat wildly struggling in his fever, is carried to a bed. The next day he is quieter. The orderly, a German, looks at him shaking his head: "Say boy, what kind of gibberish were you screaming? We thought you'd had it."

And he touches his head meaningly. Straat is very weak, he forgets all precaution.

"It's Persian," he says. "But it's not real Persian. I just think it up."

"What do you think up?"

"A language," says Straat.

So after all they saved someone who's cracked, the orderly thinks, fate is blind, great minds break, this Dutchman was lucky. And his luck holds, for the kitchen capo uses his connections and sometimes sends a crust of bread to the medical room. Straat gets back on his feet and when the orderly asks him about the language again, he pretends not to remember anything. He also hides the shock he gets when he finds out that he has lost his cap. He returns to his block, one risen from the dead, sees new faces, also on his bunk. He waits for the block senior, who shakes his hand.

"Come with me, I have something for you."

In the block senior's room, one of the floorboards has been pried loose; from under it he takes out a dirty rag, no, not a rag, a cap. Straat turns it about in his hands and feels the paper on which his language is written.

"The chap who was lying next to you, the electrician, brought it with him from the drill ground.

"Where is he?" Straat asks.

"He fell sick after you," he says. "He won't be back."

The block senior breathes as though something in his nose were broken: "You can still bring something from the kitchen. Many of the chaps here need it."

So everything continues as before. Straat reports to the kitchen squad again, Battenbach's blue eyes shine with satisfaction, Battenbach won't let anyone perish. At midday, when

Rottenfuhrer Roeder has gone, he sits down behind the table, the pencil stub in his hand, his face reflecting the meekness of the learner; to learn means *lifu*. And Straat smuggles pencil and paper and bread and potatoes through the shouting of roll call, and in the evening, his shoulder touching the shoulder of the new man next to him, he thinks up new phrases and sentences and constructs a conjugation and a declination. No longer only for Battenbach, who is satisfied with his lessons. Now it's the language itself which has gripped him. Then once more he is threatened by disclosure. Battenbach has heard that a Persian has been sent to the camp. A real Persian, Jesus! For two whole days Battenbach roams through the camp using all the tricks he knows in order to find him. Then he has him, but it's not a Persian, it's a Hindu. All day long Battenbach grumbles and curses.

"This is a damned rotten camp, it is. So much rabble and they don't even have a Persian."

"It's just that the Fuhrer hasn't got that far yet," Straat comforts him. And he thinks: Poor forsaken man from India.

Autumn comes and goes and finally it's winter. An icy wind blows across the drill ground and whirls a thin coat of snow over the frozen earth. A column in rags marches through the gate, infinitely slowly, one foot set before the other; it has come to this camp from other camps, has outlived the long march, and is now moving into the tents surrounded by wire grating, to waste away slowly under the stars high up in the skies at night, under quickly drifting clouds during the day; sometimes the sun is shining.

Behind the window of the kitchen building, where it is warm, Straat plays an imagined scene in Persian with Battenbach.

"I am a gentleman from abroad, I'm a businessman. May I have this dance with the lady? *Ta muli asa okadir. Ta muli lem basarmelko. Neli ta ramadamda donga?*"

There will come a day in May when the gates will be opened, when the chestnut trees will bloom on the avenues; the living will be able to go where they like. Straat will return to Holland, he will finish his studies in physics, become a teacher. He will tire easily his whole life long. Never again will he do anything as great as that which he accomplished here: he invented a language which he is gradually forgetting.

And Battenbach will finally get to Persia, to the empire of Iran, and he will wonder about the strange Persian one speaks there.

–translated by the author with Eva Wulff

Steve Zavodny / Volume 6, Number 1

Gloria Dyc

LANGUAGE BARRIER

Volume 6, Number 1

my grandmother spoke little english
"come and eat" was a phrase she knew
my father advised us not to refuse
an invitation to her table
"teach them the language," my mother urged
even his silence could not be translated
the air was an intoxicating broth
of sausage, cabbage and feathers
as she sat and talked in polish
vines of language grew between us
lush as the concord grapes on her fence
often she appeared critical or angry
but then she would laugh and shrug
we knew very little about her
even the length of her hair
which she kept harnessed in a bun
posed a mystery for us
my mother resented the way
she tested for dust on her visits
running a finger along dresser tops
she worked very hard on her acre
cultivating flowers, corn and raspberries
and slept deep in a feather bed
on the wall was a photo of my grandfather
retouched with pastels in an oval frame
a man we had never met: the family secret
a man who had shot himself in the basement
how were we to judge this woman
who dishonored her husband with a child
conceived in poland while he labored
in an american coal mine for an acre of land?
her stockings were opaque and salmon-colored
we had to accept the flesh beneath on faith

Charles Bukowski

ANOTHER HORSE POEM FOR ALL MY MANY DEAR FRIENDS....

Volume 6, Number 1

yes, I told them, I once rode this horse through everywhere
and his name was Nothing and we rode on through New Orleans,
St. Louis, N.Y.C., east Kansas City, you name it, you name
the city–Atlanta, that was a son of a bitch, sometimes this
horse was named Greyhound, sometimes it was just Greyhood or
Greynothing, lots of young girls always sitting with somebody
else, somebody usually dressed in a soldier's uniform looking
damned dumb to me but damned good to everybody else....
I could never get fucked, not that I wanted to, that was too
far away, I just wanted to look, to sit in a room with them,
watch the way their dresses folded as they crossed their legs
but it always became a job and not a woman, a tiny job
in a ladies dress shop or pushing bolts of cloth through
in a wooden cart through the streets of some city that
I have forgotten–up into tiny dark elevators with the cart
and the bolts of cloth, and in the elevator you worked with
a rope that had wooden spools you yanked to stop and start
the thing, and there was no light, you really had to look
good and hard to see the number of the floor written in
now-faded white chalk: 3, 6, 9, 10 ... yank, stop ... and out ...
to old neurotic-panic ladies (and forgive me) the fat
comfortable Jew with the bright suspenders and the almost-
intellectual glow ... he looked better than any of them,
even I did ...

yes, I told them, I once rode this horse through everywhere,
getting stuck now and then in all-yellow jail cells, the
yellow flecking off the bars showing spots of grey, always
the lidless toilet and a sink but the sink never worked,
just dripped water out of a faucet and you sank your
head in there and sucked at the drops when you were thirsty.

. . . Coke Cola plant in Atlanta, damn it, not wanting to be
there, not wanting to, this man saying: "I'm sorry, all
we have is this one opening, $60 a month, we'd like to
give you more but there's a government freeze on wages."

I once rode this horse through everywhere and I want you
to know that for insane people and that for certain types
of people there are never any jobs anywhere and that even
in good times, in times of war, that there is a line
9 deep for the shitiest jobs in existence . . . and that
the hardest job to find is a job as a dishwasher or a
busboy or a Western Union messenger boy.

I rode this horse, I was this horse, so I want it known.
later I was to meet women who told me, "Jesus, Bukowski,
why did you take all those dreg jobs when you could have . . ."

I hate those cunts, I hate those cunts who talk to me like
that, sitting in their offices, usually some record company,
sniffing at drugs, purses full of pills, and them acting
ultra, taking me to their apartments to fuck them, and
expecting me to love them when they have ridden their horse
through nowhere nothing exactly, and then acting betrayed
when I left them, those sliders.

. . . New Orleans, getting up at 6 a.m. after a night of 3
bottles of cheap wine and jacking-off twice, going out
on the balcony-run from your room to look for a place to
shit and shave, but each little cubicle taken, some ass
in there shaving slowly, seeing the white upon the
senseless skin of face and bone . . . waiting, and while
waiting, seeing rats as large as your hand skimming there
back and forth just before sunrise, running up and down
along the rusty iron . . . you knew your father was right,
you'd always be a bum, you had no *drive* . . .
sure, the horse got tired, you went back to bed, $4
left, something for some wine and some change left

over.

I rode this horse and I rode this horse and I knew that
for some men there would never be good times no matter
how good the times were, I knew that for some men there
would hardly ever be a woman, and for some men never a
woman forever, dying like that, and maybe better for it.

you don't know how I rode this horse, you don't know
how I met men who would fight over a piece of garbage
you wouldn't even pick up, you don't know the nights
the night jobs of working with creatures with faces
folded in like pieces of paper bags and you trying
to find something behind that paper bag and then
only finding what it looked like.

"Jesus, Bukowski, why didn't you find a job with the
media? you deliberately crucified yourself."

then, later, when I left them they claimed that I
had crucified them.

. . . even after the war, peace . . . the insane had more
trouble.

:checked a job, shipping clerk, just a block from my
room, Philadelphia, even next to my bar, I drank 2
bottles of wine, got up early, walked in and there
were 8 ahead of me

INCLUDING

one returning vet in full uniform with *all* his medals
on.
well, they hired me because I lived a block away and
they thought I'd never be late for work but I was always
late for work.

this horse, you know, I've rode him through everywhere,

I'm riding him now, smashed the glass out of the bathroom
window, my blood all up and down the stairway I chased
her all through the garden one night, throwing rocks, I
was blank naked under the blank moon, ripping plants up
by their roots, this horse, you know.

or the time blandishing about with the gangsters:
"we'll cut you in, baby, you're the toughest guy we
know.   we want you."

"listen," I told them, "I am really honored but I'm
just not interested in that sort of thing."

then I got on my horse and rode off.

what a long shot, right off the board, doesn't take
to whip, bit, blinkers, doesn't know the seven last
words of Christ, lookaway lookaway and run
6 furlongs, 7 furlongs, turf, dirt, sloppy, dry,
muddy, slow, one mile and three quarters, headwind,
overweight, bad form, gnashes fillies, friend of
Beethoven and Al Capone, I like this horse, I like
this horse very much, I do, and I'm going to enter
him in the Irish steeplechase mounted by the cardboard
figure of James Cagney strung out on and upon the
grapefruit dream.

Leah Taylor

REQUEST

Volume 6, Number 1

The radio. A greasy voice and his fleshy do-wahs
telling me "tonight, you will be mine."
He is wearing dirty underwear, I can smell it
through the speakers, someone has requested
this blast from the past.

Orange soda for breakfast, my parents in Havana,
the prickly green of late summer under my bare feet,
the Lord is supposed to be here somewhere, I am
seven years His baptized soul, I believe the birds
possess His voice, my mother His absence.

The song ends, I can see my older brother,
one leg hanging out of the opened door of the red Plymouth,
he belongs to the cigarette he is smoking, I run
through the dry grass wishing I had worn sneakers.
I am listening.

Leonard Nathan

LAST WATCH

Volume 6, Number 1

Sometimes there's a lull in the long war
between Light and Darkness, as now, September,
a day like a roomful of just-departed cigar smokers.

On the park bench sits a perfect stranger
in an overcoat of soggy brown leaves
stuck together to fit someone bulkier and dead.

Wind teases his few pale hairs.
His hands sleep one on each knee.
His face is beaten mulberry red as though by tiny hammers.

It's the eyes that bear watching. They belong on the bridge
of a rusty trawler rolling in northern waters,
expecting no landfall. The orders: watch.

He watches. It's perhaps the last duty
of the soul, the curious animal
that won't die with its eyes shut.

What does he see? Something beyond Thule,
beyond brute ice slabs and radiant blue channels–
the purity of what's there only to see.

He sees. It shines for him. He does not need it.

Steve Zavodny / Volume 6, Number 1

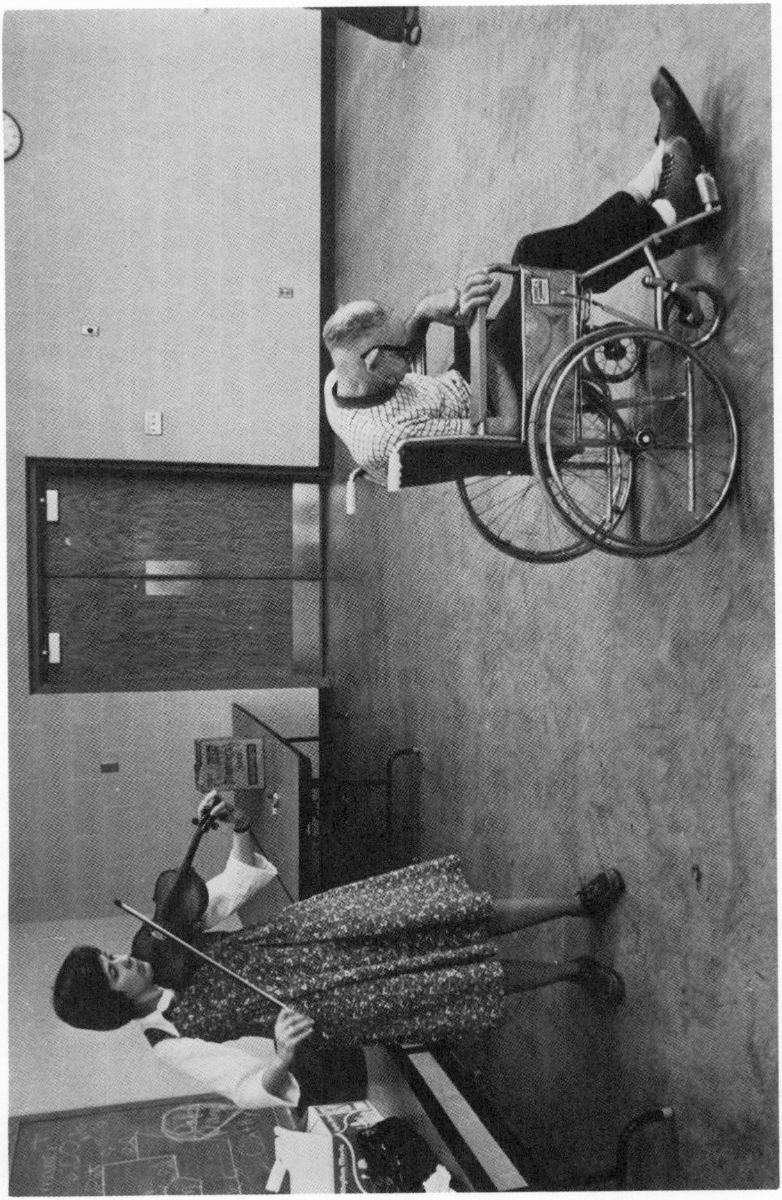

Margot Treitel

COMMON PROPERTY

Volume 6, Number 1

Food gathers in bare cupboards, silver gleams.
Books lean against each other on a common shelf.

Rich smells of egg and cheese and sweat
and sex and smoke float around the place.

There's even a heavy sweetness over meals.
A scrapbook fills with snapshots, the printed
whole first year of life.

Even quarrels about nothing fill up space.
Thin cries of hunger, how we fill each other's needs.

This is such ordinary life. Why bother to
record it. Nothing's happened in this house
that hasn't happened up and down the whole block.

So lying in bed now and cherishing this
contempt for all familiarity, I tell you

this is how great discoveries are made.
By accident. Exactly here, pacing from room to room,
going out to get the paper. Simply by

standing and stirring coffee, thumbing through
books to get a little knowledge for its own sake,

hanging over a sick child who will not die,
over everything that works imperfectly but
can now be used.

Ai Qing

THE TRANSLUCENT NIGHT

Volume 6, Number 1

1

The translucent night.

. . . laughter flares up from the dikes . . .
A mob of drinkers racketing towards
the village asleep—
the village,
and the barking of dogs sets
the diffuse stars up there to trembling.

The village—
the streets sleeping,
the square sleeping
and they burst into the wide-awake tavern.

Wine, lamps, faces of sots,
lascivious guffaws . . .

"Let's make it over
to the slaughterhouse and have
some beef soup . . ."

2

The drinkers touch the edge of the village,
enter an open door where light is coming out,
odor of blood, piled meat, malodorous warmth of cowhide,
clamor of men, clamor of men.

Like wildfire the oil lamp discloses
these several muddy faces
who live in the pastures.

This is our recreation park,
these are our familiar faces,
we hold the simmering bones of beef
and bite down with large mouths.

"Wine, wine, wine—
pass that bottle to me—"

Like wildfire the oil lamp discloses
the cow's blood, the butcher's bloody arms,
his forehead all blood-stained.

Like wildfire the oil lamp discloses
our flaming muscles, and within,
the power of pain, anger and hate.

Like wildfire the oil lamp discloses
in every corner the wakeful
ones of the night, the drunks, drifters,
passing bandits, cattle rustlers . . .

"Wine, wine, wine—
pass that bottle to me—"

"Under the trembling stars let's
make it over to . . ."
Laughter flares up from the dikes . . .
The mob of drunks has left
the village in its slumber and
rackets towards the

night, the translucent
night!

1932; translated from the Chinese by Hualing Nieh

Jarkko Laine

A FOOTNOTE TO SHAKESPEARE'S HAMLET

Volume 6, Number 1

Word. It turns in a comprehensible form
everything that the eye, the ear takes out of the world,
that the mind sees in the jungle of dreams.
In the beginning was the word, Majesty,
it was but the act that gave birth to chaos,
all the generations
that in a man are waiting for their coming.
Now they want to deprive me of this knowledge,
to make me accept as a lie
what I'm living as a truth every day.
I'm not selling my word. I have eaten it.
I ate it like an actor eats a line,
then spits the skins in the face of his audience.
In the beginning, a word, and now it's inside me,
in me, and I'm on my way to the port,
away from here, away from the grave of my father.
Word, hand of the heart, it's moving now.
It's bending, raising the hatchet,
it's dangerous now, this word, that was eaten
and became flesh.
I, too, am the Son of Man,
but my word is not to be sold,
and it does not betray me against my wish.
I may be mad, but I'm no fool,
I don't believe in the skulls
when they are talking in the voice of History.
To hell with all skulls,
make a cemetery wall out of them,
scare old wives and children with them,
just don't insist to me
that the wisdom of the ancients is speaking through them.
Skull of the Teacher, yes, sure,
but his scholarly expression

didn't outlive his skin.
His wisdom lies inside worms now,
or in grass, chewed by a dull ruminant.
You're not fooling me.
I'm afraid of the soldiers, the bone-shirts,
therefore I'll take a ship and sail away,
and it's not soldiers that frighten me, but the word,
the word they are obeying.
That word was taken from my father
when they shovelled dirt into his mouth,
and they asked a price for that word, and it was sold.
Now it's a dagger in a hand,
it will sink between my shoulders
if I don't leave, sail away.
When I came here, I came as an heir,
and immediately they thought that I,
like a whore, was willing to sell my only possession,
this word, my life.
I can sign a paper, put my name on it,
for I have no part in my name
nor in my birth, in this body of mine
that was created by chaos, by an act.
They wanted to buy my word
but I seized it, and I ate it.
Now they want my life
as they took the life of my father,
though they'll gain nothing by that:
they'll get a skin full of scars,
a pile of entrails
that even the augurs aren't using anymore.
But they want it, my life,
so they can misuse my word
like they have misused my father's word,
therefore I'll take a ship, and sail away,
to conceive, or to write
so that the word would live
so that the act would be naked,

always, skinned from its clothes,
for everyone to see.

—translated by John Currie with the author

Luellen Fletcher

A FATHER'S TRYST

Volume 6, Number 1

A man whistles his child to dinner
knowing she will appear magically
from beyond the lattice of swings
to leap a deer's leap
over his fence, then pause for a kiss
in the hush of her landing.
His waiting is weary,
sagging beneath the streetlamp,
he is swollen cheeks, chafed roads,
glasses chinked but still trusted
for seeing. Bills, work,
his wife's impossible drawbridge,
another six o'clock crisis
diluted in the panic of living
prick him like a globe of gnats
until the child tumbles out,
a clutter of innocence, tan,
anklets fluttering down, mud
on her pink, open blouse
and his arms shoot out suddenly
as if he has been uprooted,
or grapples to retrace a secret
he never meant to share.

Alberto Vanasco

THIRTY YEARS AND THEIR DAYS

Volume 6, Number 1

This day has loosened a shadowy leaf of the year
it has emptied a dark and sticky substance of time over me
and face to face we have kept ourselves on guard

therefore the afternoon is as clear as childhood quarrels
and encourages a smile worth more than the clatter of a thousand
    little resentments

thirty years of so many things which do not add up to a day

in things written and remembered
in dawn propped up by a dream
in vague enterprises and infallible deals
in tenderness scattering through the afternoons without direction
in the ardor for algebra which carried me through so many years
in the shelter of the mountain ridge
in love confined by time
in my soldiers who listened because I was one of them
in the obstinacy of roulette which will break someday
in a son's laughter burning in air
in the friendship of poets which is the best part of poetry
so many years in the few days which add up to nothing
because we are not made if not for the sun of childhood
if not for the long street cut off in mystery
a woman leaning against destiny
a blind horse melting in summer
the gaze of a dark and silent man
a gesture a bird disheveled by memory
an unknown hand upon the face

so many things in the few days which do not add up to a year

suddenly an old story rises up in us

a corner of the past lit by a carnival
a confused boy wandering in sand drifts
a gate open towards nowhere
a strong admiration which is patient and silent

so many days in the few things which do not add up to a lifetime

the solitude which has asked for us every instant

because it is time to reach everyone
time to call someone
to be him
time like a hand to touch the world
and to seek a word like the earth

a word to become one with us
to explain justice and please mankind

thirty years of so many things which do not add up to a day

But we have before us the uncertainty of our myths
the failure of our revolutions
the pride of our evanescence
and the imperious necessity of life.

We have before us an America alive
in armored cells of blood
and in the triumph of patience.

And so we enter fully into the subject of good poetry.

Of good health in good hands.

Of good deeds of friendship.

Of good reasons for poetry.

Of good poetry for the best of reasons.

1955 & 1962; translated by Abbey Wolf

Alvaro de Campos (Fernando Pessoa)

"THEY HAD NO ELECTRICITY THERE,"

Volume 6, Number 1

They had no electricity there,
and so it was by the flickering light of a candle
that I, in bed already, read
the only thing I could find to read–
a Bible, in Portuguese curiously enough, especially for Protestants.
I reread the First Epistle to the Corinthians.
All around me the exaggerated peace of the provincial night
filled my mind with noise and tumult.
In that peace my own desolation brought me to the verge of tears.
The First Epistle to the Corinthians–
I read it again by candlelight that suddenly looked as old as time,
and a sea of emotions groaned within me.
Me, I'm nothing, an empty fiction.
What should I ask of myself and the rest of the world?
"If I have no charity . . ."
Sovereign light shines forth, and from the bosom of centuries comes
that great message that can make the soul free–
"If I have no charity . . ."

But me, I have no charity.

–translated from the Portuguese by Erskine Lane

Elizabeth Pickard-Ginsberg / 36% of original / supplement

Marianne Wolfe (Waldman)

A MOON ON THE WATER

The Poem You Asked For

Clinging to my breast, no stronger
Than a snail snuggly curled.
—Vassar Miller

I relax into the bentwood rocker
And take you back. The rocker,
Catching us, sends us forward. Motion
Takes over and I forget
That I am not still. You don't seem to understand
'Still' after nine months
In the tumultous womb: you scream for motion.

You cling to me like a frog to its rock,
Knees and elbows bent, still struggling to unfold.
How strange your weight feels
After so many months of rocking
With a lover. How tiny
And yet how human you are
With your little ears no bigger than prunes

And hands and mouth that search
For my small breasts, as milkless as your thumb.
I am not your mother, though
You don't seem to understand 'mother';
You give and grope unknowingly, without distinction.
You sigh,
And I feel you tremble against me as a moon on the water.

Pat Dooley, visual; Vassilis Zambaras, poem

Poetry-With-Drawings In The Buses placards & postcards (supplement)

James Ochs, visual; Anna Akhmatova, poem; Leonard Opalov, transl.

Poetry-With-Drawings In The Buses placards & postcards (supplement)

I POSSESS

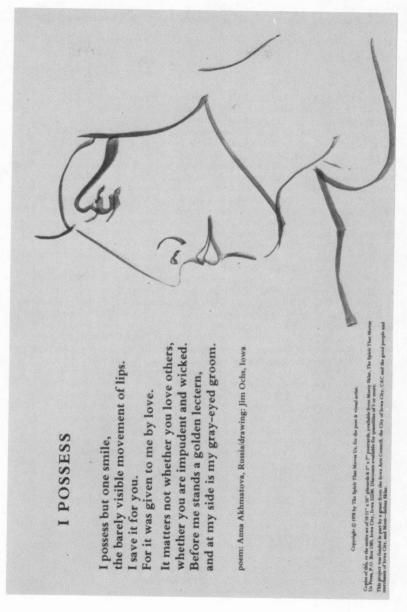

I possess but one smile,
the barely visible movement of lips.
I save it for you.
For it was given to me by love.

It matters not whether you love others,
whether you are impudent and wicked.
Before me stands a golden lectern,
and at my side is my gray-eyed groom.

poem: Anna Akhmatova, Russia/drawing: Jim Ochs, Iowa

Copies of this, or the entire set of 10 11" x 16" placards & 5" x 7" postcards, available from Morty Sklar, The Spirit That Moves Us Press, P.O. Box 1585, Iowa City, Iowa 52240. Discounts available for quantities of 5 or more.

This project was funded in part by a grant from the Iowa Arts Council, the City of Iowa City, CAC and the good people and merchants of Iowa City, and Mom—Selma Sklar.

Notes on Contributors

Because of limited space, bibliographical information usually indicates only one publication. Entries are also made for translators.

Persons wishing to contact a contributor should write to The Spirit That Moves Us Press.

AKHMATOVA, Anna. 1889-1966. One of Russia's great poets.
ALVAREZ, Carlos Hermosilla. b. 1900. A leading etcher in Chile.
ANONYMOUS. Took "family album" photo in 1936.
ARA, Agneta. b. 1945 in Helsinki, where she still lives. Published *The Heart of the Horse* in 1979. Writes in Swedish. Worked as a secretary at the Bank of Finland.
BATKI, John. b. 1942. Translated *Attila Jozsef: Poems & Texts*, U. of Iowa Press.
BERTOLINO, James. b. 1942. His poem also appeared in *Precinct Kali & The Gertrude Spicer Story*, New Rivers Press. Editor of *Cincinnati Poetry Review*.
BLACKMORE, Mike. b. 1954. An artist attending medical school at the U. of Iowa.
BRUCE, Lennart. b. 1919 in Stockholm. *The Broker* (poems), Panjandrum Press.
BRUCHAC, Joseph. b. 1942. *The Good Message of Handsome Lake*, Unicorn Press. Editor of *The Greenfield Review*. Taught in west Africa 1966-1969.
BUKOWSKI, Charles. b. 1920 in Germany. *Ham on Rye* (novel), Black Sparrow P.
CLAYTON, Charles. Nothing about this translator is known to us.
COOPER, Dennis. Edits *Little Caesar*. Leader of rock group, *The Same*. From The Crossing Press, his *The Tenderness of the Wolves* (poems).
CURRIE, John. Teaches English & creative writing at Hobart & William Smith.
DANA, Robert. b. 1929. *What the Stones Know*, Seamark Press.
DAUMIER, Honore. Painting is reproduced with permission of Musee du Louvre.
DOOLEY, Pat. b. 1950. Artwork for *Heavy Jars*, by Anselm Hollo, Toothpaste P.
DOTY, Catherine. b. 1952. Published in *rara avis, Hanging Loose, Intro 8*.
DYC, Gloria. b. 1950. *Freshtones: An Anthology of Poetry, Fiction, Essays by Women*, One & One Communications. An editor of *Moving Out*, feminist journal.
ELLIOTT, Harley. b. 1940. *Darkness at Each Elbow*, Hanging Loose Press.
FAREWELL, Patricia. Freelance copywriter. No updated biog. note received.
FAULKNER, Margherita Woods. b. 1926. *Timepeace* (poems), Juniper Press.
FLETCHER, Luellen. b. 1957. English teacher at an alternative h.s. in Boulder.
FOX, Hugh. b. 1932. *Leviathan*, Carpenter Press. Editor of *Ghost Dance*.
GEORGE, Emery. b. 1933. Translated Miklos Radnoti's *The Complete Poetry*, Ardis. Born Budapest. Professor of German, U. of Michigan, Ann Arbor.
GLEN, Emilie. b. 1937. *Roast Swan* (collected works, poems), Rutherford Books.
GRAY, Darrell. b. 1945. *Scattered Brains* (poems), Toothpaste Press. *Essays & Dissolutions*, Abraxas Press. Co-editor of *The Actualist Anthology*, Spirit That Moves.
GRIGORESCU, Joana. Nothing about this translator is known to us.
GRIMES, Michael. b. 1951. Acquisitions librarian at Ohio State University.
GUMILEV, Nikolai. 1886-1921. Founder of the Acmeists literary movement in Russia. Shot to death by the Cheka.
HARDING, Gunnar. b. 1940. Jazz musician, painter, poet, translator. Swedish.
HARRISON, James. Visual artist in N.Y.C. Two paintings in Harkness Gallery.
HEAD, Bessie. b. 1937 in South Africa. This story was published in *The Collector of Treasures*, Heinemann AWS, London.
HELDENBRAND, Sheila. b. 1951. *Savelli Editori* (anthology), Rome.
HILTON, David. b. 1938. *Huladance*, The Crossing Press.
HOAGLAND, Tony. *Love Slams* (poems), self-published by letterpress.

HOLLO, Anselm. b.1934 in Helsinki. *With Ruth in Mind*, Station Hill Press. Professor, Poetics Program, New College of California, San Francisco.
HOLTON, Milne. Nothing about this translator is known to us.
HONGO, Garrett Kaoru. b.1951 in Hawaii. *Yellow Light* (poems), Wesleyan U. Press. Director, Asian Exclusion Act, a theater group.
JACKSON, William Haywood. b.1930. *Fellow Travelers* (poems), Samisdat.
JOVANOVSKI, Meto. b.1928 in Macedonia. *The Path to Loneliness* (stories), 1979. Books of his stories & novels published in Romania, Slovenia, Croatia.
JOZSEF, Attila. 1905-37. Born in Budapest. *Attila Jozsef: Poems & Texts*, translated by John Batki; Carcanet Press (Europe) & U. of Iowa Press.
KELLER, Madeleine. b.1947. Co-editor of *Knock Knock* poetry anthology.
KESSLER, Jascha. b.1929. *Death Comes for the Behaviorist: 4 Novellas*, Lexis P.
KINSELLA, W.P. b.1935 in Canada. *Shoeless Joe* (novel), Houghton Mifflin.
KLOEFKORN, William. b.1932. *Alvin Turner As Farmer* (poems), Windflower P. His poem also appeared in *Brother Songs*, Holy Cow P., & *Chowder Review*.
KOEHNE, David. b.1956. Published in *Mademoiselle; Police Beat*.
KOERTGE, Ronald. b.1940. *Selected Poems*, U. of Arkansas Press.
KOHLHAASE, Wolfgang. b.1937 in Berlin.This story also appeared in *New Year's Eve with Balzac* (collected stories), Aufbau-Verlag and Luchterhand-Verlag.
KORNBLUM, Allan. b.1949. *The Salad Bushes* (poems), Seamark Press. Co-editor and -publisher with Cinda Kornblum, of The Toothpaste Press.
KORNBLUM, Cinda. b.1950. *Bandwagon* (Toothpaste P.; poems). See above.
KOSTELANETZ, Richard. b.1940. *New and Selected Poems*, BkMk Press.
KRESH, David. b.1940. *Bloody Joy: Love Poems*, Slow Dancer Press (England)
LADANYI, Mihalyi. b.1934 in Hungary. *Behind the Armies* (selected poems),1976
LAINE, Jarkko. b.1947 in Finland. *Amerikan Cowboy* (poems), Otava. Editor of *Parnasso*, a literary magazine in Finland.
LANE, Erskine. b.1940. *Game-Texts: A Guatemalan Journal*, Gay Sunshine Press
LUNDKVIST, Lars. b.1928 in Sweden. *Modern Swedish Poetry*, U. of Minnesota P.
MANDELSTAM, Osip. b.1891 in Warsaw; died c.1938 near Vladivostok. *Kamen* and *Tristia* (both poetry), publisher not cited. One of the Russian Acmeist poets.
MANFRED, Freya. b.1944. *American Roads* (poems), Overlook (Viking Press)
MARSHALL, Jack. b.1936. *Arriving on the Playing Fields of Paradise* (poems), Jazz Press; *Versions from Rumi* (adaptations), Blue Teal Press (Canada)
MEAD, Stuart. b.1955. Artwork in *Luna Tack*. Editor of *Diaper Rash*.
MILLER, A.McA. Published poems in *The Beloit Poetry Journal; Buckle*.
MILLER, Chuck. b.1939. *Oxides* (poems), Seamark Press
MONTAG, Tom. b.1947. *Between Zen & Midwestern* (poems), Saltworks Press
MORICE, Dave. b.1946. *Quicksand through the Hourglass* (poems), Toothpaste P.
MORRIS, Richard. b.1939. *The Fate of the Universe* (non-fiction), Playboy Press
MULAC, Jim. b.1942. Poetry in *Me Too; Dental Floss*. Co-editor with Morty Sklar, of *Editor's Choice: Literature & Graphics from the U.S. Small Press, 1965-1977*, The Spirit That Moves Us Press
NATHAN, Leonard. b.1924. This poem also appeared in *Holding Patterns*, U. of Pittsburgh Press
NIEH, Hualing. Editor of *Literature of the Hundred Flowers*, Columbia U. Press
NORTH, Susan. b.1940. *All That Is Left* (poems), Desert First Works.
OCHS, James. b.1943. Artwork for *Re-Examination of Freedom*, Toothpaste P.
OPALOV, Leonard. b.1904 in Latvia. Poems & translations in *The Literary Review; Bitterroot; The Christian Science Monitor; Trace*. Retired factory worker.
PACERNICK, Gary. b.1941. Poetry in *North American Review; Poetry Now*
PESSOA, Fernando. Considered the greatest Portuguese-language poet since Camoes.
PHILLIPS, Walt. b.1936. *Some Poems*, Befuddled Press.
PICKARD-Ginsberg, Elizabeth. Biographical data not available to us.

PIERCY, Marge. b. 1936. *Circles on the Water* (poems), Knopf. Poems in *The Aspect Anthology*, Zephyr Press.
POTTS, Charles. b. 1943. *Rocky Mountain Man*, The Smith; *Valga Krusa*, Litmus.
QING, Ai. b. 1910 in China. *Selected Poems*, Peking (1956 & 1979)
RAY, David. b. 1932. *The Tramp's Cup* (poetry), The Chariton Review Press
RAY, Judy. Biographical information not received.
RIOS, Alberto. b. 1952. His poem also appeared in *Whispering to Fool the Wind*, Sheep Meadow. He was the recipient of the Walt Whitman Award, 1981
ROSS, Marty. We have lost contact with this poet.
SCHUSTER, Sylvia. Lives and works in N.Y.C. Prolific visual artist.
SESSIONS, David. American, painting and drawing in England the past two years.
SIMMER, Scott. b. 1951. Poems in *New Letters; Prairie Schooner; Poetry Now*.
SJOBERG, John. b. 1944. *Hazel* (poems), Toothpaste Press
SKLAR, Morty. b. 1935. *The Night We Stood Up for Our Rights* (poems), Toothpaste Press. Co-editor with Jim Mulac, of *Editor's Choice: Literature & Graphics from the U.S. Small Press, 1965-1977*, The Spirit That Moves Us Press
SKLOOT, Floyd. b. 1947. *Rough Edges*, Chowder Chapbooks
SMITH, Edward. b. 1941 in China. *Going* and *The Flutes of Gama* (poems), Litmus
SPECTOR, Merrill. b. 1943. Living and painting in Philadelphia.
STUART, Floyd. b. 1940. Poet, with essays in *The Atlantic Monthly; Harper's Mag.*
STRUTHERS, Ann. b. 1930. Poet, anthologized in *A-Z*, Swallow Press
STUTTS, Paul. b. 1952. Artist, working as model and cook/waiter.
TAYLOR, Leah. b. 1950. Poems in *Gravida; Yellow Brick Road; Poets On*
TEETER, Audrey. b. 1935. Poems in *Suction; Social Development Issues*
TOIU, Constantin. b., and living in, Romania. No bibliographical data available.
TREITEL, Margot. b. 1935. Poems in *Chicago Review; Denver Quarterly*
UNGER, Barbara. b. 1932. *The Man Who Burned Money* (poems), Bellevue Press
VANASCO, Alberto. b. 1925 in Buenos Aires. *Canto Rodado* (publisher not cited)
WOLF, Abbey. Nothing is known to us about this translator.
WOLFE, Marianne (name now Waldman). b. 1952. *The Berrypicker*, Copper Canyon Press. Teaches in a cooperative pre-school. Owned an expresso coffeehouse.
WULFF, Eva. Nothing is known to us about this translator.
ZAMBARAS, Vassilis. Lives in Greece. This poem also appeared in *Sentences*, Querencia Books
ZAVODNY, Steve. b. 1947. *The Life and Times of Steven Alan Zavodny*, self-published portfolio of photographs.
ZU-BOLTON, Ahmos. b. 1948. *A Niggered Amen* (poems), Solo Press.

* * *

Complete Index to
The Spirit That Moves Us magazine,
Volumes I-VI (1975-1982)
& the supplements: *The Poem You Asked For*, by Marianne Wolfe & *Poetry-With-Drawings in the Buses* placards & postcards

Other indexes, grouping contributors according to the issues in which they appear, are included in this publication.

Only titles which are not poetry are designated by category.

When a poem has no title or is titled "Poem," the first several words or the entire first line is shown.

Following a translator's name, the translated author is given, not the work, unless more than one person has translated the same author in the same issue.

The Actualist Anthology is Volume 2, Numbers 2 & 3.

Cross-Fertilization: The Human Spirit As Place is Volume 5, Number 3.

The Farm in Calabria, by David Ray, is part of Volume 5, Numbers 1 & 2 (printed back-to-back, with its own cover and typeface).

A The Spirit That Moves Us *Reader: Seventh Anniversary Anthology* is Volume 6, Numbers 2 & 3.

Hoagland, Tony	"Sympathy for the buddha"	3/3
	"I Said"	3/3
	"Poem" ("A rat blunders...")	3/3
	"After Wordsworth"	3/3
	"When Travelling"	*Reader* & 3/3
Hogan, Michael	"With a Prison Work Gang"	2/1
Holland, Barbara	"Water Baby"	1/1
	"As One Possessed"	1/3
Hollo, Anselm	translator of Lars Lundkvist	*Reader* & 1/3
	"Song of the Tusk"	*Reader & Actualist Anthology*
	"The Empress Hotel Poems"	*Actualist Anthology*
	"A Warrant Is Out for the Arrest of Henry Miller"	ibid
	"through two layers of glass"	ibid
	"The Discovery of LSD a True Story"	ibid
	"Strange Encounter"	ibid
	"Scriptual I"	ibid
	"Los Sedentarios"	ibid
	"Good Stuff Cookies"	ibid
	"Elegy"	*P-W-D* placs. & pstcds. & *Actualist Anthology*
	translator of Gunnar Harding	4/2&3
Holton, Milne	translator of Meto Jovanovski	*Reader* & 5/1&2
Hongo, Garrett Kaoru	"And Your Soul Shall Dance"	*Reader&Cross-Fertilization*

I

Inman, Will	"To Winds Marked in the Hill"	*Cross-Fertilization*

J

Jackson, Haywood	"Out of the Deepness"	*Reader & Cross-Fertilization*
Jammes, Francis	"The sun made the well-water..."	6/1
Johns, Bethany	"Apologetic"	4/1
	"Five Weeks in Little Tibet"	4/1
Johnson, Sandi	"Give Me Your Situation an I'll Give You Mine"	1/2
Jovanovski, Meto(story)	"The Man in the Blue Suit"	*Reader* & 5/1&2
Jozsef, Attila	"Dusk"	*Reader* & 1/1
	"Since You've Been Away"	1/1
	"The Seventh"	1/2
	"Encouragement"	1/2

K

Kalasz, Marton	"Maiden"	3/3
Kann, Cary	pen & ink drawing	2/1
	2 pen & ink drawings	*P-W-D* placs. & pstcds.
Keller, David	"Diccionario"	3/1&2
	" 'Money Is a Kind of Poetry' "	3/1&2
Keller, Madeleine	"Ancestria"	*Reader* & 1/1
Kessler, Jascha	translator of Mihalyi Ladanyi	3/3
	translator of Marton Kalasz	3/3
(story)	"Rhadamanthys"	*Reader* & 4/2&3
(story)	"The Foundation"	4/2&3
Kilsheimer, Diana	"Wedding Summer"	1/3
Kinsella, W.P. (story)	"Caraway"	*Reader* & 3/1&2
Kloefkorn, William	"Out-and-Down Pattern"	*Reader* & 5/1&2
Koehne, David	"Loup-Garou"	*Reader* & 2/1
Koertge, Ronald	"Demands of the Molars"	*Reader* & 4/1
	"The Haunted Aisle"	4/1

L

M

Pickard-Ginsberg, Eliz.	pencil drawing, cover	*Reader* & *The Poem You Asked For*
Piercy, Marge	"The Cast Off"	*Reader* & 3/3
Porter, Bern	linoleum print	4/2&3
Potts, Charles	"Migratory"	1/2
	"La Chartreuse"	1/2
	"I Dream of Oaxaca"	*Reader* & 2/1

Q

Qing, Ai	"The Translucent Night"	*Reader* & 6/1
	"Snow Falls on China"	6/1

R

Radnoti, Miklos	"Friday"	3/3
Ray, David	"In Victoria Station"	3/3
	"The Father"	3/3
	"A Gypsy Lady in Mexico"	*The Farm in Calabria* & 3/3
	"Train"	*The Farm in Calabria*
	"The Castaways"	ibid
	"Cobalt"	ibid
	"Marriage"	ibid
	"In the Back Yard"	ibid
	"The Landscape"	ibid
	"The Whip"	ibid
	"The Farm in Calabria"	ibid
	from "The Kids With the Milk"	ibid
	"Hay Harvest in Calabria, at the Time of the Vietnam War"	ibid
	"Adelina's Lament"	ibid
	"Mulberries"	*Reader* & *The Farm in Calabria*
Ray, Judy	2 photographs (1 a cover)	1 in *Reader* & both in ditto
Reyes, Carlos	translator of Pablo Neruda	1/3
	from "The Travelers"	2/1
Rilke, Rainer Maria	from "The Blind Woman"	1/1
	"Rilke's Complaint"	3/1&2
Rios, Alberto	"Morning"	*Reader* & 4/1
	"El Molino Rojo"	4/1
	"Yaqui"	4/1
Roberts, Len	"Earth Blue and Brown and Silent Now"	3/1&2
Rodriguez, Aleida	"Bruja"	*P-W-D* placs. & pstcds.
Rodriguez, W. R.	"Grandfather: A Photograph"	6/1
	"Luck Enough"	6/1
Ross, Marty	"Bo Diddley at Forty-Seven"	*Reader* & 4/1

S

Sanders, Scott (story)	"The Fire Woman"	*Cross-Fertilization*
Schneider, Steven	translator of Dario Semper	1/2
Schulze, John	photograph	*Cross-Fertilization*
Schuster, Sylvia	pencil drawing, cover	*Reader* & 4/1
Schwartz, Jeffrey	"La Turista"	6/1
Semper, Dario	"Tigers"	1/2
Sessions, David	8 pen & ink drawings	1 in *Reader* & all in 1/2
	pencil drawing, cover	*Reader* & 2/1
	5 pen & ink drawings	3/3
	pen & ink drawing	*P-W-D* placs. & pstcds.
Sexauer, Roxanne	pen & brush & ink drawing	*P-W-D* placs. & pstcds.

Sheets, Dan	"It happened one night . . ."	5/1&2
Simmer, Scott	"Fourth of July Address./Deserted Railroad Tunnel, Colorado./Continental Divide."	*Reader* & 4/1
Sjoberg, John	"The Death of Democracy"	*Actualist Antho.* & 1/1
	"Some Poems My Day Off"	1/3
	"We try not to touch so close . . ."	*Reader* &*Act. Antho.*
	"Pablo Anytime"	*Actualist Anthology*
	"Fantastic Collection of Stamps"	ibid
	"Overalls"	ibid
	"An Answer"	ibid
	"Thoughts"	ibid
	"Paffer Jocker"	ibid
	"Blue Tit"	ibid
	"Porch Window"	ibid
	from "The Living Sea Scroll"	4/2&3
Sklar, Morty	"7:30 wanting"	1/1
	"Howard Johnson's in the Poconos"	1/1
	"Bed"	1/1
	"Land of the Blind"	1/1
	photograph, cover	*Reader* & 1/2
	"Closer"	1/2
	"Laura"	1/3
	"The Smell of Life"	*Cross-Fert.* & *Act. Antho.* &1/3
	"Jarashow"	*Actualist Anthology*
	"Poem Without the Word Love"	ibid
	"Charlie Parker"	ibid
	"I Put the Telephone Back on Its Receiver"	ibid
	"Modern Times"	*Reader* & *Actualist Anthology*
	"Mending"	*Actualist Anthology*
	"In Memory of My Being Late"	ibid
	"So This Is Earth"	ibid
	"Ma"	ibid
	"McDonald's"	3/3
(essay)	"Actualism, and the Movement As Restaurant"	*Cross-Fert.*
Skloot, Floyd	"Executive Search"	*Reader* & 3/1&2
Smith, Edward	"Enlargement"	*Reader* & 2/1
Smith, Joan	"Listening to the Radio"	2/1
Smith, Larry	collage	5/1&2
Somerville, Jane	"The Wishing War"	3/3
Sovrin, Julia	"The Bomb"	1/1
	"In Shantytown"	1/1
Spector, Merrill	2 linoleum prints	*Reader* & *Cross-Fertilization*
Stelzig, Eugene	translator of Hermann Hesse	2/1
Stephens, Jim	"Last Poem"	2/1
Stewart, Bob	"The Point Coupee Funeral Home"	*Cross-Fertilization*
Stokes, Daniel	"Note to a Country Western Singer"	1/3
Struthers, Ann	"The Dance"	*Reader* & 3/3
Stryk, Lucien (conversations)	"Conversations with Zennists"	4/1
Stuart, Floyd	"The Wives"	*Reader* & 3/1&2
Stutts, Paul	2 woodcuts	1 in *Reader* & both in 5/1&2
Suk, Julie	"Dogs Do Bark"	3/1&2
Suni	"Genaro"	2/1
Supervielle, Jules	"Seizure"	3/3

T begins on next page

Woessner, Warren	"Parvin State Park"	1/3
Wolf, Abbey	translator of Alberto Vanasco	*Reader* & 6/1
Wolfe, Marianne	"A Moon On the Water"	*Rdr.* & *The Poem You Asked For*
	"Riddle"	*The Poem You Asked For*
	"Entering Iowa"	ibid
	"Masks"	ibid
	"Posing"	ibid
	"The Marriage Debt"	ibid
Wolff, Daniel	"Autumns Used to Darken With Meaning"	5/1&2
Wulff, Eva	translator of Wolfgang Kohlhaase	*Reader* & *Cross-Fertiliz.*

X

the only letter that doesn't mark the spot

Y

Yates, Barbara	"Five Ways Out"	2/1
Yunus, Bakhrum	translator of Frans Nadjira	6/1

Z

Zambaras, Vassilis	"Crow's Foot"	3/1&2
	"The Poet As Archaeologist"	3/1&2
	"Poetry Lesson"	*Reader* & *P-W-D* pl. & p'c. & 3/1&2
Zavodny, Steve	3 photographs (1 cover)	2 in *Reader* & all in 6/1
Zawadiwsky, Christine	"The Blind Train"	1/3
Zima, Elizabeth	"Photo Liz"	1/2
Zu-Bolton, Ahmos	"The Basketball Star"	*Reader* & 3/1&2

Indexes According to Issues

The Spirit That Moves Us

(transl. = translator)

Volume 1, Number 1

Volume 1, Number 2

Volume 1, Number 3

Volume 2, Number 1

Aal, Katharyn Machan
Anderson, Jack
Beining, Guy
Coad, Kermit
Conner, Ann
Epstein, Glen
Eshleman, Clayton
Evans, Jerri
Gersmann, Joel
Harbaugh, Gary
Hesse, Hermann
Hix, Hubert
Hogan, Michael
Kann, Cary
Koehne, David
Kostelanetz, Richard
Locke, R. J.
Manfred, Freya
Montag, Tom
Nissan, Bobby
O'Donnell, Patty
Oksol, Connie
Potts, Charles
Reyes, Carlos
Sessions, David
Smith, Edward
Smith, Joan
Stelzig, Eugene (transl.)
Stephens, Jim
Suni
Thomas, Lisa
Tuschen, John
Veitch, Tom
Yates, Barbara

The Actualist Anthology (Volume 2, Numbers 2 & 3)

Batki, John
Dooley, Pat
Gray, Darrell
Heldenbrand, Sheila
Hilton, David
Hollo, Anselm
Kornblum, Allan
Kornblum, Cinda
Mattingly, George
Miller, Chuck
Morice, Dave
Mulac, Jim
Sjoberg, John
Sklar, Morty
Toth, Steve

Volume 3, Numbers 1 & 2

Abrams, Doug
Akhmatova, Anna
Alvarez, Carlos Hermosilla
Aragon, Louis
Bertolino, James
Bruchac, Joseph
Catullus, Gaius Valerius
Collins, Billy
Cook, Geoffrey (transl.)
Cook, Paul
Cooper, Dennis
Ditsky, John
Elliott, Harley
Faulkner, Margherita Woods
Filoche, Jean-Luc (transl.)
Fox, Hugh
Gollub, Christian-Albrecht (transl.)
Grierson, Patricia
Grimes, Michael
Hanson, Jim (orig. & transl.)
Henderson, Riley
Keller, David
Kinsella, W. P.
Lourie, Iven
Lucina, Sister Mary
Marcus, Mordecai
Miller, Brown
Mladinic, Peter
Morris, Richard
Morrison, Madison
North, Susan
Opalov, Leonard (transl.)
Osborne, Ken
Pacernick, Gary
Rilke, Rainer Maria
Roberts, Len
Skloot, Floyd
Stuart, Floyd
Suk, Julie
Torgersen, Eric
Tucker, Martin
Tulloss, Rod
Walsh, Charlie
Will, Frederic
Zambaras, Vassilis
Zu-Bolton, Ahmos

Volume 3, Number 3

Brewer, Kenneth
Carter, Jared
Dana, Robert
George, Emery (transl.)
Goldiner, Jim
Harrison, James
Head, Bessie
Hoagland, Tony
Kalasz, Marton
Kessler, Jascha (transl.)
Kresh, David
Ladanyi, Milhalyi
Langton, Daniel J. (transl.)
Ludwin, Peter
Mandelstam, Osip
McIntosh, Joan
Niditch, B. Z.
Piercy, Marge
Radnoti, Miklos
Ray, David
Sessions, David
Sklar, Morty
Somerville, Jane
Struthers, Ann
Supervielle, Jules
Unger, Barbara

Volume 4, Number 1

Anthony, Donald
Burt, John
Campion, Daniel
Ehrenburg, Ilya
Johns, Bethany
Koertge, Ronald
McCoy, Maureen
Medina, Pablo
Miller, Chuck
Opalov, Leonard (transl.)
Rios, Alberto
Ross, Marty
Schuster, Sylvia
Simmer, Scott
Stryk, Lucien
Tarlen, Carol
Vinz, Mark

Volume 4, Numbers 2 & 3

Ara, Agneta
Bruce, Lennart (orig. & transl.)
Clayton, Charles (transl.)
Cummins, Eric
Elliott, Harley
Glen, Emilie
Grigorescu, Joana (transl.)
Harding, Gunnar
Hasselstrom, Linda
Hollo, Anselm (transl.)
Kessler, Jascha
Kornblum, Allan
Linden, Gurli
Mead, Stuart
Miller, Chuck
Mulac, Jim
Okai, Atukwei
Porter, Bern
Sjoberg, John
Toiu, Constantin

Volume 5, Numbers 1 & 2

Albright, Jeff
Blackmore, Mike
Brown, Fred
Hester, M. L.
Hionis, Argyris
Holton, Milne (transl.)
Jovanovski, Meto
Kloefkorn, William
Kohlberg, Madonna
Kornblum, Allan
Kunze, Reiner
Mead, Stuart
Mulac, Jim
Sheets, Dan
Smith, Larry
Stutts, Paul
Thalenberg, C. E. (transl.)
Wolff, Daniel

The Farm In Calabria (published back-to-back with, and part of, *V. 5, Nos. 1 & 2*)

Ray, David
Ray, Judy

Cross-Fertilization: The Human Spirit As Place (Volume 5, Number 3)

Bruce, Lennart
Cuelho, Art
Daumier, Honore
Hewitt, Geof
Hongo, Garrett Kaoru
Inman, Will
Jackson, Haywood
Kohlhaase, Wolfgang
McKain, David
Mead, Stuart
Miller, A. McA.
Sanders, Scott
Schulze, John
Sklar, Morty
Spector, Merrill
Stewart, Bob
Velarde, Ramon Lopez
Waage, Fred
Whittington, Gary (transl.)
Wulff, Eva (transl.)

Volume 6, Number 1

Akerlund, Eric
Anderson, Jack
Bertolino, James
Brewer, Kenneth
Bukowski, Charles
Burt, John
Chin, Marilyn (transl.)
Cochran, William
Cummings, Michael
Currie, John (transl.)
Davies, Nancy
Davis, David Aaron
Dyc, Gloria
Fletcher, Luellen
Frost, Celestine
Fuchs, Gunter Bruno
Jammes, Francis
Lacaba, Jose F.
Laine, Jarkko
Lane, Erskine (transl.)
Lense, Edward
Lifshin, Lyn
McCullough, Ken
Miller, Jane
Miner, Tom
Mosemann, Barbara A.
Nadjira, Frans
Nathan, Leonard
Nieh, Hualing (transl.)
Oldknow, Antony (transl.)
Oliver, Kenneth (transl.)
Pessoa, Fernando
Pfingston, Roger
Qing, Ai
Rodriguez, W. R.
Schwartz, Jeffrey
Taylor, Leah
Treitel, Margot
Tuttle, Lynn
Urioste, Pat K.
Vanasco, Alberto
Winston, Bonnie
Wolf, Abbey (transl.)
Yunus, Bakhrum (transl.)
Zavodny, Steve

The Spirit That Moves Us *Reader: Seventh Anniversary Anthology (Volume 6, Numbers 2 & 3)*

Akhmatova, Anna
Alvarez, Carlos Hermosilla
Anonymous
Ara, Agneta
Batki, John (transl.)
Bertolino, James
Blackmore, Mike
Bruce, Lennart (orig. & transl.)
Bruchac, Joseph
Bukowski, Charles
Clayton, Charles (transl.)
Cooper, Dennis
Currie, John (transl.)
Dana, Robert
Daumier, Honore
Dooley, Pat
Doty, Catherine
Dyc, Gloria
Elliott, Harley
Farewell, Patricia
Faulkner, Margherita Woods
Fletcher, Luellen
Fox, Hugh
George, Emery (transl.)
Glen, Emilie
Gray, Darrell
Grigorescu, Joana (transl.)
Grimes, Michael

Gumilev, Nikolai
Harding, Gunnar (transl.)
Harrison, James
Head, Bessie
Heldenbrand, Sheila
Hilton, David
Hoagland, Tony
Hollo, Anselm (orig. & transl.)
Holton, Milne (transl.)
Hongo, Garrett Kaoru
Jackson, Haywood
Jovanovski, Meto
Jozsef, Attila
Keller, Madeleine
Kessler, Jascha (orig. & transl.)
Kinsella, W. P.
Kloefkorn, William
Koehne, David
Koertge, Ronald
Kohlhaase, Wolfgang
Kornblum, Allan
Kornblum, Cinda
Kostelanetz, Richard
Kresh, David
Ladanyi, Milhalyi
Laine, Jarkko
Lane, Erskine (transl.)
Lundkvist, Lars
Mandelstam, Osip
Manfred, Freya
Marshall, Jack (transl.)
Mead, Stuart
Miller, A. McA.
Miller, Chuck
Montag, Tom
Morice, Dave
Morris, Richard
Mulac, Jim
Nathan, Leonard
Nieh, Hualing (transl.)
North, Susan
Ochs, James
Opalov, Leonard (transl.)
Pacernick, Gary
Pessoa, Fernando
Phillips, Walt
Pickard-Ginsberg, Elizabeth
Piercy, Marge
Potts, Charles
Qing, Ai
Ray, David
Ray, Judy
Rios, Alberto
Ross, Marty
Schuster, Sylvia
Sessions, David
Simmer, Scott
Sjoberg, John
Sklar, Morty
Skloot, Floyd
Smith, Edward
Spector, Merrill
Struthers, Ann
Stuart, Floyd
Stutts, Paul
Taylor, Leah
Teeter, Audrey
Toiu, Constantin
Toth, Steve
Treitel, Margot
Unger, Barbara
Vanasco, Alberto
Wolf, Abbey (transl.)
Wolfe, Marianne
Wulff, Eva (transl.)
Zambaras, Vassilis
Zavodny, Steve
Zu-Bolton, Ahmos

The Poem You Asked For, by Marianne Wolfe (chapbook supplement)

Wolfe, Marianne
Pickard-Ginsberg, Elizabeth

Poetry-With-Drawings in the Buses (placards & postcards supplement)

Akhmatova, Anna
Bly, Robert
Dooley, Pat
Doty, Catherine
Grierson, Patricia
Harrison, James
Hollo, Anselm
Kann, Cary
Miller, Jane
Ochs, James
Opalov, Leonard (transl.)
Osborne, Ken
Rodriguez, Aleida
Sessions, David
Sexauer, Roxanne
Tulloss, Rod
Zambaras, Vassilis

*

Notes on the Editor

photo: John Riley

Morty Sklar was born in New York City in 1935. In 1971 he left New York on his 1967 Honda "Dream" with no other objectives than the National Poetry Festival in Allendale, Michigan, and to find a place to live. At the Festival he met someone who said Iowa City was a "nice place to live." And when he got to Iowa City he found that person's judgement to be correct for himself. He soon became caught up in the non-academic community of writers and editors which thrived most wholly from the early to mid 1970s.

In 1975 Morty published the first issue of *The Spirit That Moves Us*. In 1977 both his *The Night We Stood Up for Our Rights: Poems 1969-1975* (The Toothpaste Press) and *The Actualist Anthology* (co-edited with Darrell Gray; 14 poets who lived and interacted in Iowa City from the early to mid 1970s; The Spirit That Moves Us Press) were published. In 1980 he co-edited with Jim Mulac, *Editor's Choice: Literature & Graphics from the U. S. Small Press, 1965-1977* (The Spirit That Moves Us Press). His poetry has been anthologized in *A-Z: 200 Contemporary American Poets*, edited by David Ray (Swallow Press; a *New Letters* book; 1981) and *Brother Songs*, edited by Jim Perlman (Holy Cow! Press; 1979), and has also appeared in *The New York Quarterly; Little Caesar; Abraxas; Gum; Suction* and other magazines. Parts of his novel, *Getting Up*, have appeared in *The American Microcosm*, co-edited by Joseph Bruchac and Michael Hogan (*The Greenfield Review*) and *First Person Intense*, edited by Sasha Newborn (The Mudborn Press; 1978).

In 1966 Morty helped found Phoenix House, a therapeutic community for heroin addicts, in New York City. Previous to that he was a heroin junkie from 1960-1966.

He married Shelley Sterling-Sklar in 1981.